Judi Sunderland and Leann Co

ESSENTIALS
GCSE Child Development

Contents

Contents

What is a Family?

What a Family Provides

1 Which of the following should be provided by a family? Tick the correct options.

    A   Socialisation skills ⬭

    B   Child benefit ⬭

    C   Physical and health care ⬭

    D   Food, clothing and shelter ⬭

    E   Nursery care ⬭

    F   Routine developmental assessments ⬭

    G   Love, affection and comfort ⬭

    H   Poor role models ⬭

2 What does co-habit mean?

....

3 Explain the difference between primary and secondary socialisation.

....

....

....

Types of Family

4 Circle the correct option in the following sentences.

    a) In a **nuclear / lone-parent** family, parents and children live together in the home.

    b) A one-parent family is **always / sometimes** made up of a mother and her children.

    c) Children **can / can't** be adopted by same sex couples.

5 Choose the correct words from the options given to complete the following sentences.

    both   **two**   **joint**   **shared care**

In a .... family, children live in ....

households and spend time with .... parents. .... decisions

are made about them.

Foster and Residential Care

Looked After Children

1 What is meant by 'looked after' children?

....

....

2 Which of the following are reasons why children **may not** live with their birth families? Tick the correct options.

    A   The child has a slight disability   ◯

    B   The parents are divorced   ◯

    C   The child has been physically abused   ◯

    D   The child has been disciplined   ◯

    E   The child's parents are dead   ◯

    F   The child's single parent is in prison   ◯

    G   The child has been neglected   ◯

    H   The child's parents have gone on holiday   ◯

Foster Families

3 Which of the following statements is correct? Tick the correct option.

    A   Foster families only care for children in the short term   ◯

    B   Foster parents have the same legal rights as birth parents   ◯

    C   Foster parents are checked by social services   ◯

    D   Foster parents must have children of their own   ◯

Residential Care Homes

4 Choose the correct words from the options given to complete the following sentence.

    exception   **short-term**   **residential**   **severe**

.... care homes provide .... care for children, with the

.... of children with .... disabilities or behavioural problems.

◯

Family Structure and Roles

Why are Family Structures Changing?

1 Circle the correct options in the following sentences.

a) Unmarried mothers and co-habitation have become **more / less** socially acceptable.

b) Divorce laws are now **more complex / simpler**.

c) There are **fewer / more** benefits available to single parents.

Family Roles

2 Fill in the missing words to complete the following sentences.

Whether your sexual role is decided by _____ (your genes) or nurture

(the _____ you are brought up in) is debatable. Both are influential.

3 Which of the following are traditional expectations for girls? Tick the correct options.

A To get dirty and grubby ◯

B To cry if hurt ◯

C To be noisy and boisterous ◯

D To be physically active ◯

E To play with dolls ◯

F To be clean, neat and tidy ◯

G To be brave if hurt ◯

H To be well-behaved and quiet ◯

Culture

4 Explain what is meant by the word culture.

_____

5 Choose the correct words from the options given to complete the following sentence.

> **culture**　　　　**multicultural**　　　　**ethnic groups**

In a _____ society like Britain, there are many different _____

_____, all with their own special _____ .

Questions to Consider

1. Which of the following statements are true? Tick the correct options.

   Before having a baby, ideally you should have...

   A   a stable relationship with your partner ☐

   B   an immature attitude to life ☐

   C   money to buy equipment for a baby ☐

   D   lots of friends with children ☐

   E   suitable housing ☐

   F   a hectic lifestyle ☐

   G   a holiday abroad ☐

   H   realistic expectations of your lifestyle with children ☐

2. Explain what having children can bring to a relationship.

   ....

   ....

3. Is the following statement **true** or **false**?

   Babies that aren't planned aren't necessarily unwanted. ....

Bad Reasons for Having a Baby

4. Circle the correct option in the following sentences.

   a)   A **good / bad** reason for having a baby is to have someone to love.

   b)   A **good / bad** reason for having a baby is to prove you are mature.

   c)   A **good / bad** reason for having a baby is because you have a stable relationship.

   d)   A **good / bad** reason for having a baby is to have someone who will love you.

5. Explain what is meant by the phrase 'biological clock is ticking'.

   ....

   ....

☐

Contraception

What is Contraception?

1 Circle the correct option in the following sentences.

a) The type of contraception people choose depends on **age / fertility.**

b) A long-term method of contraception is **always / sometimes** needed.

c) The contraceptive method you choose can depend on your **religious beliefs / religious knowledge.**

d) Your health **can / can't** affect your choice of contraception.

2 Choose the correct words from the options given to complete the following sentences.

sterilisation   **women**   **vasectomy**   **cutting**   **pregnancy**

.... can be prevented by .... This is done by

.... or blocking the fallopian tube in ...., or the sperm tube

in men (...).

3 Name two methods of emergency contraception that may be used after unprotected sex.

a) ....

b) ....

Natural Methods

4 How do natural methods of contraception, i.e. natural family planning (NFP), work?

....

....

5 Which of the following are NFP methods? Tick the correct options.

A Ovulation monitor ⬭   **B** Diaphragm ⬭

C Cervical mucus ⬭   **D** Vasectomy ⬭

E Calendar method ⬭   **F** Temperature method ⬭

G Sterilisation ⬭   **H** Morning-after pill ⬭

Facts About Contraception

1 Which of the following statements are true? Tick the correct options.

    A   A femidom is worn by a man ⬭

    B   An IUD protects from STIs ⬭

    C   A diaphragm should be used with spermicidal gel / cream ⬭

    D   A contraceptive injection is effective for a month ⬭

    E   There are no possible side effects with an IUS ⬭

    F   A contraceptive implant slowly releases progestogen ⬭

    G   The combined pill contains oestrogen and progestogen ⬭

    H   A male condom can't be damaged ⬭

2 Explain why a male condom isn't 100 percent effective.

....

....

3 Circle the correct option in the following sentences.

    a) Condoms **are / aren't** free from family planning clinics.

    b) There are **some / no** health risks from the side effects when a diaphragm is used.

    c) There **is / isn't** an antidote for a contraceptive injection if a woman changes her mind.

    d) An IUD **does / doesn't** work immediately.

4 Fill in the missing words to complete the following sentences.

The combined pill contains .... and ....

The .... pill contains progestogen only.

5 Which three methods of contraception need to be fitted by a doctor?

    a) ....

    b) ....

    c) ....

Male Reproductive System

Male Reproductive System   OCR

1 Circle the correct option in the following sentences.

   a) The **sperm duct / urethra** transports semen and urine out of the body.

   b) The **scrotum / foreskin** is removed in circumcision.

   c) The **prostate gland / penis** adds fluid to sperm to form semen.

   d) The **foreskin / scrotum** allows sperm to be stored at a lower temperature than body heat.

2 Which of the following statements are true? Tick the correct options.

   A Another name for sperm duct is seminal vesicle ⬭

   B The scrotum hangs outside the body ⬭

   C Testosterone is produced by the penis ⬭

   D The penis is flaccid when not sexually stimulated ⬭

   E The scrotum covers the end of the penis ⬭

   F Sperm is produced by the testis ⬭

   G Circumcision is the removal of the sperm duct ⬭

   H Semen and urine can't mix during intercourse ⬭

Producing and Releasing Sperm

3 Choose the correct words from the options given to complete the following sentences.

ejaculation   prostate gland   fluid

epididymis   ducts   seminal vesicles   sperm

_____ is produced by the testes and stored in the _____ .

At _____ , sperm is released and rushes through the _____ .

As it passes along the tube, the _____ and the

_____ _____ release seminal _____ .

4 Explain why sperm need seminal fluid.

_____

Female Reproductive System

Female Reproductive System

1 Circle the correct option in the following sentences.

a) A baby girl **is / isn't** born with a store of eggs in her ovaries.

b) After the menopause, women **can / can't** get pregnant naturally.

c) The quality of eggs **deteriorates / improves** with age.

d) Eggs start to be released at **menopause / puberty**.

2 Which of the following statements are true? Tick the correct options.

A The vagina increases in size during pregnancy ◯

B The funnel wafts released eggs into the fallopian tube ◯

C Fertilisation takes place in the vagina ◯

D The vagina weighs approximately 30g ◯

E The endometrium is another name for the lining of the uterus ◯

F The vagina leads from the outside of the body to the cervix ◯

G The ovaries are controlled by testosterone ◯

H The cervix is a strong ring of muscle ◯

3 Describe the uterus.

....

....

The Menstrual Cycle

4 The following are stages of the menstrual cycle. Number the stages **1–5** to put them into the correct order. The first one has been done for you.

A If a fertilised egg doesn't appear, the uterus lining breaks down. ◯

B The uterus lining remains thick, waiting for a fertilised egg. ◯

C Egg is released (ovulation). ◯

D The uterus lining starts to gradually thicken up again. ◯

E The uterus lining breaks down (a period). ①

Pre-conceptual Care and Conception

Pre-conceptual Care

1 What is the basis for pre-conceptual care?

_____

_____

2 Which of the following should parents-to-be do? Tick the correct options.

A Avoid passive smoking ⬭

B Only take recreational drugs occasionally ⬭

C Not drink alcohol ⬭

D Check for immunity to chicken pox ⬭

E Eat a diet low in fibre ⬭

F Exercise for general fitness ⬭

G Not smoke ⬭

H Lead a healthy lifestyle ⬭

3 Choose the correct words from the options given to complete the following sentences.

spina bifida   **wholegrain**   **three months**   **folic acid**   **green**

A _____ _____ supplement should be taken

_____ _____ before conception to prevent

_____ _____ in the baby. Folic acid and folate can be found in

leafy _____ vegetables, nuts, beans, and _____ bread and cereals.

Conception

4 Which of the following statements is correct? Tick the correct option.

A A blastocyst implants itself in the fallopian tube ⬭

B A zygote implants itself in the uterus wall ⬭

C When an egg and sperm fuse, a zygote is formed ⬭

D Implantation takes place 14–16 days after fertilisation ⬭

Genetics

Basic Genetics

1 Fill in the missing words to complete the following sentence.

Genes may be _____ (strong) or recessive (_____).

2 Circle the correct option in the following sentences.

a) Recessive genes are **strong / weak**.

b) Chromosomes **are / aren't** made up of genes.

c) Sex cells have **23 / 46** chromosomes.

d) Genes **do / don't** carry information that determines eye colour.

Genetic Counselling

3 Circle the correct option in the following sentences.

Genetic counselling is offered if…

a) the mother has **two / five** or more miscarriages.

b) ante-natal screening shows a(n) **normal / abnormal** result.

c) a couple are **distantly / closely** related.

d) there is a history of **infectious / inherited** diseases.

Inheritance of Sex

4 Which of the following statements are true? Tick the correct options.

A   An egg fertilised by an X carrying sperm will become a girl

B   There is a much greater chance of an egg being fertilised by a Y sperm

C   Gender is determined by sex hormones

D   Sperm cells carry only Y chromosomes

E   Half of all egg cells carry Y chromosomes

F   Gender is determined by sex chromosomes

G   An egg fertilised by a Y carrying sperm will become a boy

H   The number of male and female babies is approximately equal

Early Stages of Pregnancy

Confirming Pregnancy

1 Which of the following is a possible sign of pregnancy? Tick the correct option.

- **A** Craving certain foods ⬭
- **B** Being hungry all the time ⬭
- **C** A sudden dislike of certain tastes and smells ⬭
- **D** Feeling depressed ⬭

Pregnancy Testing

2 Fill in the missing words to complete the following sentence.

To take a pregnancy test, an absorbent sampler is placed in a mid-stream _____

_____ to detect the presence of the hormone _____ .

Estimated Delivery Date

3 Circle the correct option in the following sentences.

a) The letters EDD stand for **early dating details / estimated delivery date**.

b) To calculate the EDD, add **290 / 280** days to the first day of the last period.

c) **39−43 / 37−42** weeks is the length of a normal pregnancy.

d) A reliable indication of the EDD can be given by an **X-ray / early dating scan**.

Losses in Pregnancy

4 Which of the following statements are true? Tick the correct options.

- **A** Miscarriage is the loss of pregnancy before 28 weeks ⬭
- **B** A baby born dead after 20 weeks is a stillborn baby ⬭
- **C** An abortion results in the birth of a baby ⬭
- **D** Viable means unable to survive ⬭
- **E** An ectopic pregnancy occurs if a fertilised egg implants itself in the fallopian tube ⬭
- **F** Up to 80 per cent of miscarriages happen in the first 12 weeks of pregnancy ⬭
- **G** A baby is viable after 24 weeks ⬭
- **H** A miscarriage is the medical process of ending a pregnancy ⬭

Multiple Pregnancies

1 Choose the correct words from the options given to complete the following sentences.

uterus   **naturally**   **fertility**   **one**   **likely**

Multiple pregnancies take place when more than .... foetus develops in the

.... They can occur .... , but are more

.... to take place if .... treatment is used.

2 What is the term used for...

a) two multiple birth children? ....   **b)** three multiple birth children? ....

c) four multiple birth children? ....   **d)** five multiple birth children? ....

e) six multiple birth children? ....

Twins

3 Which of the following statements are true? Tick the correct options.

A Fraternal twins are always the same sex ⬭

B Identical twins have the same genes ⬭

C Conjoined twins are the result of two eggs being fertilised ⬭

D Identical twins have the same blood group ⬭

E Fraternal twins result if one egg is fertilised ⬭

F Fraternal twins can be different sexes ⬭

G Two separate fertilised eggs produces identical twins ⬭

H Fraternal twins don't look alike ⬭

Possible Complications

4 Circle the correct option in the following sentences.

a) Multiple pregnancies **always / often** result in low birth weight.

b) **Premature / Delayed** labour is a possible complication with a multiple pregnancy.

c) The need for a Caesarean section is **reduced / increased** with a multiple pregnancy.

d) A multiple pregnancy **decreases / increases** the risk to the mother's health.

A Healthy, Comfortable Pregnancy

What To Do

1 Which of the following factors isn't important when choosing a pregnancy bra? Tick the correct option.

A Support ◯

B Adjustable ◯

C Fashion ◯

D Wide straps ◯

What to Avoid

2 Circle the correct option in the following sentences.

a) Alcohol in pregnancy can cause **MMR / FAS**.

b) Drugs in pregnancy can cause **mental impairment / food poisoning**.

c) Smoking in pregnancy has been linked to **AIDS / SIDS**.

d) Eggs eaten by pregnant women should be **lightly / hard** boiled.

3 Choose the correct words from the options given to complete the following chart.

salmonella   miscarriage   liver and liver products   undercooked meat   caffeine

Foods to Avoid	Problem	Effect
Eggs, unless hard boiled; products containing raw egg		Food poisoning
Unpasteurised milk; incorrectly reheated cook-chilled foods	Listeriosis	........................, still birth, severe illness
	Vitamin A	Too much harms the baby
	Toxoplasmosis	Miscarriage; stillbirth; blind baby
Coffee		Miscarriage; low birth weight

4 Which of the following statements are true? Tick the correct options.

A Drinking alcohol in pregnancy may cause a stillbirth ◯

B Taking drugs in pregnancy results in a calm baby ◯

C Drinking alcohol in pregnancy may cause the baby to have facial abnormalities ◯

D Smoking can cause a miscarriage ◯

Causes of Infertility

1 Fill in the missing text to complete the following chart.

Cause	Problem
	Sperm can't reach the egg
No ovulation / hormone imbalance	
	Egg won't be fertilised

Assisted Conception

2 Circle the correct options in the following sentence.

A gynaecologist has **specialist / new** knowledge of the functions and **problems / diseases** of the female **reproductive / contraceptive** system.

3 Choose the correct words from the options given to complete the following sentences.

uterus   **test tube**   **surgically**   **eight**   **hormone**   **fallopian tube**

In IVF (*in vitro* fertilisation), you must first have _____ treatment. Then eggs are

_____ removed, and penetrated by sperm in a _____

_____ . At _____ cell division, they are placed in the

_____ or _____ (GIFT).

4 Which of the following statements are true? Tick the correct options.

A In egg donation, the woman's own eggs are used ◯

B In IVF, eggs are surgically removed ◯

C In donor insemination, sperm from the husband is used ◯

D In ICSI, an individual sperm is injected directly into an egg ◯

E A surrogate mother keeps the baby after birth ◯

F PGD is a procedure used to screen embryos for genetic disorders ◯

G In surrogacy, the birth mother doesn't keep the baby ◯

H In PGD, embryos are examined for infectious diseases ◯

▢

Development of Unborn Child

Length of Pregnancy

1 What are the three trimesters of pregnancy (in months)?

a) ....

b) ....

c) ....

Weeks 6 to 12

2 Which of the following statements is true about a 6-week old embryo? Tick the correct option.

A It swims by kicking ◯   **B** Its heart is beating ◯

C It's eight inches long ◯   **D** It can suck its thumb ◯

3 Circle the correct option in the following sentences.

a) At 8 weeks, the arms **can / can't** be seen.

b) At 8 weeks, the foetus **can / can't** swim by kicking.

c) At 12 weeks, the foetus **has / doesn't have** well developed sex organs.

d) At 12 weeks, the foetus has its eyes **open / closed**.

Weeks 24 to 36

4 Explain the difference between lanugo and vernix.

....

....

5 The diagram shows a baby in the cephalic position. Match parts **A, B, C, D, E** and **F** with the labels **1–6** on the diagram.

A Pubic bone ◯

B Liver ◯

C Bladder ◯

D Diaphragm ◯

E Intestine ◯

F Spine ◯

Development of Unborn Child

Placenta

1 Circle the correct option in the following sentences.

a) The placenta **is / isn't** produced by a fertilised egg.

b) The placenta **is / isn't** the only disposable organ in the body.

c) The placenta **is / isn't** also known as the afterbirth.

d) The placenta weighs about **250g / 500g**.

2 Which of the following statements are true? Tick the correct options.

A The placenta provides the baby with carbon dioxide ⬭

B Viruses pass through the placenta ⬭

C The placenta has a poor blood supply ⬭

D The placenta provides food for the baby ⬭

E The placenta stops alcohol passing to the baby ⬭

F Oxygen gets into the mother's blood through the placenta ⬭

G The placenta removes waste from the baby ⬭

H The placenta is about 2.5cm thick ⬭

Amniotic Sac and Umbilical Cord

3 Choose the correct words from the options given to complete the following sentences.

| 37°C | bangs | sac | cushions | fluid |

The amniotic _____ is filled with amniotic _____, which keeps the

baby's temperature at _____. It _____ and protects the baby from

_____.

4 Explain what happens to the umbilical cord after birth.

_____

_____

Ante-natal Tests and Scans

Tests and Checks

1 Which of the following are symptoms of pre-eclampsia? Tick the correct options.

- **A** Blurred vision ☐
- **B** Protein in the urine ☐
- **C** Bladder infection ☐
- **D** Swelling of the legs ☐
- **E** High blood pressure ☐
- **F** Excessive weight gain ☐
- **G** Dehydration ☐
- **H** Varicose veins ☐

2 How can a foetal heartbeat be checked?

....

....

3 What do blood tests in pregnancy check for? Tick the correct options.

- **A** Anaemia ☐
- **B** Eclampsia ☐
- **C** Protein ☐
- **D** HIV ☐
- **E** Rubella immunity ☐
- **F** Meningitis immunity ☐
- **G** The mother's blood group ☐
- **H** The baby's blood group ☐

Scans

4 Choose the correct words from the options given to complete the following sentences.

number   size   cord   confirms   heartbeat   position   exact

Scanning .... pregnancy and gives the .... foetal age and

.... It checks the .... of foetuses. It also checks the

........................., umbilical .... and ....

of the placenta.

Tests During Pregnancy

Screening Tests

1 Which of the following statements are true? Tick the correct options.

A An increased risk of spina bifida could be indicated by high AFP levels ☐

B Excess fluid on the back of the neck could indicate Down's syndrome ☐

C Screening tests can't show an increased risk of abnormality ☐

D The triple / quadruple test is a blood test ☐

E Excess fluid in the uterus could indicate spina bifida ☐

F AFP measurements are used with the baby's age
to estimate the possibility of Down's syndrome ☐

G Diagnostic tests can confirm the findings of screening tests ☐

H The nuchal fold translucency test is a blood test ☐

Diagnostic Tests

2 Choose the correct words from the options given to complete the following sentences.

15–19   **amniotic**   **needle**   **amniocentesis**   **uterus**   **ultrasound**

An .... test is normally done at .... weeks of pregnancy.

A sample of .... fluid is removed using an .... scan and

a hollow .... inserted into the ....

3 Name four things that fluid from an amniocentesis test is examined to detect.

a) ....

b) ....

c) ....

d) ....

4 Which test removes a sample of placenta tissue?

....

Health Care for Mum and Baby

Midwives

1 Circle the correct option in the following sentences.

a) Midwives deliver babies in **complicated / straightforward** births.

b) Midwives **may / may not** administer some drugs.

c) Midwives carry out **specialist / routine** tests.

d) Midwives run **ante-natal / post-natal** classes.

2 Explain the difference between the work place of a community midwife and a maternity unit midwife.

....

....

Medical Practitioners

3 Which of the following statements are true? Tick the correct options.

A A GP shares responsibility for a pregnant woman with a midwife ☐

B A GP delivers babies in a straightforward birth ☐

C A GP conducts the post-natal examination ☐

D A GP has specialist knowledge of infertility ☐

Hand Held Notes

4 Which of the following is an advantage of hand held notes? Tick the correct option.

A They can only be accessed by the mother ☐

B All information is stored in one place ☐

C They remind the mother of her next ante-natal appointment ☐

D They aren't detailed ☐

5 Circle the correct option in the following sentences.

a) Hand held notes include the **hospital / home** address.

b) Hand held notes are **invaluable / useless** in an emergency.

c) Hand held notes contain **ante-natal / post-natal** tests.

d) Hand held notes contain information about **IVF / EDD**.

☐

© Lonsdale

Preparing for Birth

Ante-natal Classes

1 Circle the correct option in the following sentences.

a) Ante-natal classes are usually held in the **first / last** eight weeks of pregnancy.

b) Ante-natal classes are run by **health visitors / midwives**.

c) Ante-natal classes **are / aren't** a good way of meeting other mums to be.

d) Ante-natal classes **do / don't** provide advice on fertility treatment.

The Role of the Father

2 List three things a father-to-be can do to support his partner during pregnancy.

a) ....

b) ....

c) ....

Birth Plan

3 What would a woman record on her birth plan?

....

....

4 Which of the following are found on a birth plan? Tick the correct options.

A   Growth charts of the baby   ◯

B   Family history   ◯

C   Type of pain relief preferred   ◯

D   Baby's name   ◯

E   Dietary requirements   ◯

F   Views on episiotomy   ◯

G   Whether the baby will be given a Vitamin K injection   ◯

H   Who will cut the cord   ◯

Home Births

Home Births

1 Which of the following are reasons why it would be inadvisable to have a home birth? Tick the correct options.

- **A** First baby ◯
- **B** Pets in house ◯
- **C** High blood pressure ◯
- **D** Age of mother ◯
- **E** Previous Caesarean ◯
- **F** Diabetes ◯
- **G** Multiple birth ◯

Preparing for a Home Birth

2 Choose the correct words from the options given to complete the following sentences.

temperature   **midwife**   **birthing pool**   **protective**

In a home birth, the .... will advise about the .... in the

room, what .... materials are needed, and the correct use of a

....

3 Which of the following items **wouldn't** be found in a home birth pack? Tick the correct option.

- **A** Sterile cord clamps ◯
- **B** Drugs ◯
- **C** Scissors ◯
- **D** Cotton drapes ◯

4 Circle the correct option in the following sentences.

a) A midwife delivers a sterile sealed birth pack for a home birth about **two weeks / one month** before the birth.

b) A midwife brings oxygen for a home birth in case the baby needs **resuscitating / rescuing**.

Advantages of Hospital Births

1 Which of the following are advantages of a hospital birth? Tick the correct options.

A Emergency equipment available ◯

B Privacy ◯

C Unlimited visiting ◯

D No cooking ◯

E Familiar surroundings ◯

F Midwife always available ◯

G Epidural available ◯

H Lots of people can be present at the birth ◯

Home-from-Home Suites

2 What are home-from-home suites designed to look like?

....

3 Circle the correct option in the following sentences.

a) Home-from-home suites can help to make the mother **relax / pain free**.

b) Some home-from-home suites have **single / double** beds so the father can stay.

c) Home-from-home suites are only suitable for **high / low** risk births.

d) Home-from-home suites are **always / sometimes** available.

Domino Delivery Scheme

4 Fill in the missing words to complete the following sentences.

In a domino delivery scheme, a .... accompanies the mother to

.... and delivers the baby.

If there are no ...., the midwife returns home with the ....

and baby .... hours later.

Pain Relief Drugs in Labour

Epidural Anaesthetic

1 In an epidural, where is the plastic tube placed?

_____

2 Which of the following is an advantage of having an epidural? Tick the correct option.

A May cause headaches ⬭

B Stops all pain quickly ⬭

C Can only be given in hospital ⬭

D May increase length of labour ⬭

Pethidine

3 Choose the correct words from the options given to complete the following sentences.

muscle   **control**   **bottom**   **drug**   **placenta**   **injected**   **drowsy**

Pethidine is a _____ that is _____ into a deep

_____ in the leg or _____ to relieve pain. The disadvantages are

that the baby may be born _____ as the drug crosses the _____,

and the mother can feel out of _____.

Entonox (Gas and Air)

4 Which of the following statements about entonox are true? Tick the correct options.

A It's harmful to the baby ⬭

B The mother may feel sick ⬭

C It removes all pain ⬭

D It works immediately ⬭

E It's inhaled through a mask or mouth piece ⬭

F It wears off quickly ⬭

G It contains nitrous oxide ⬭

H The mother may have a dry mouth ⬭

Alternatives to Drugs in Labour

TENS Machine

1 Which of the following is not a disadvantage of a TENS machine? Tick the correct option.

- **A** Can't be used in water births ◯
- **B** Harmful side effects ◯
- **C** Doesn't work on intense pain ◯
- **D** Mother can't shower during labour ◯

Water Birth

2 Fill in the missing words to complete the following sentences.

A water birth takes place in a _____ _____, which looks like a

large _____ or paddling pool. The water is kept at a constant temperature of

_____.

A water birth may not always give adequate _____ relief, and isn't always available

in _____.

Other Kinds of Pain Relief

3 Name three natural kinds of pain relief that can be used during labour.

a) _____

b) _____

c) _____

4 Circle the correct options in the following sentence.

The **advantages / disadvantages** of other kinds of pain relief are that they **may / may not** be effective, and training is needed from **qualified / unqualified** people.

Labour

What is Labour?

1 Choose the correct words from the options given to complete the following sentences about labour.

hormones   **birth**   **cervix**   **baby**   **mother**   **uterus**

Labour is the process of giving _____, which is started by _____.

The _____ has to work hard so that the contractions of the _____

can open the _____, and the _____ can be pushed out.

Stage 1 of Labour

2 Which of the following may occur in Stage 1 of labour? Tick the correct options.

A   The show   ◯

B   Urge to push   ◯

C   Contractions   ◯

D   Waters breaking   ◯

E   Baby's head crowning   ◯

F   Backache   ◯

G   Placenta being delivered   ◯

H   Nausea   ◯

3 What colour is the amniotic fluid?

_____

4 Fill in the missing words to complete the following sentence.

When your waters break, the _____ _____ comes out of the

_____ when the _____ sac bursts. It may come in a slow

_____ or sudden _____.

Stage 2 of Labour

1 What is an episiotomy?

_____

2 Which of the following **doesn't** occur during Stage 2 of labour? Tick the correct option.

    A The baby is a separate person   ◯

    B The head is born gradually   ◯

    C The placenta is delivered   ◯

    D The mother has the urge to push   ◯

3 Circle the correct options in the following sentences.

    a) Very **mild / strong** contractions push the baby along the birth **canal / tunnel**.

    b) The head is born **quickly / gradually**.

    c) When the **narrowest / widest** part of the head comes out of the **vagina / uterus**, it's known as crowning.

Stage 3 of Labour

4 Fill in the missing words to complete the following sentences.

In Stage 3 of labour an _____ of oxytocin may be given to the mother to stop

excessive _____, and help the _____ and remaining cord to be

delivered quickly. This takes 5–15 minutes of _____.

5 What is examined before labour is complete? Tick the correct option.

    A The umbilical cord   ◯

    B The placenta   ◯

    C The uterus   ◯

    D The vagina   ◯

Birth Complications

Position of the Baby

1 Which of the following is a simple position for a baby to lie in? Tick the correct option.

A Oblique ☐   B Breech ☐

C Head down ☐   D Transverse ☐

2 Circle the correct option in the following sentences.

a) The **breech / oblique** position is when a baby's legs or bottom are first.

b) In the transverse position, the baby lies upside down **in / across** the uterus.

c) Babies can **always / sometimes** be manoeuvred into the head down position.

Induction

3 Which of the following statements are true? Tick the correct options.

A When labour is induced, it starts immediately ☐

B Induction can involve sweeping or artificially rupturing of the membranes ☐

C Induction may be used if a baby is overdue (term + 10–12 days) ☐

D Labour may be induced if the baby is in the wrong position ☐

E A prostaglandin pessary can be used to induce labour ☐

F Induction is a natural way of starting labour ☐

G Labour may be induced if the placenta isn't working properly ☐

4 Which hormone is used to induce labour?

....

Assisted Delivery

5 Explain the difference between a Ventouse and a forceps delivery.

....

....

....

....

What is a Caesarean Section?

1 Choose the correct words from the options given to complete the following sentences.

| uterus | abdominal | bikini | operation | removed |

A Caesarean section is an _____ that cuts open the _____ wall

and the _____ along the _____ line, so the baby can be

_____ .

2 Name the two types of Caesarean section.

a) _____   **b)** _____

3 Which of the following statements are true? Tick the correct options.

A Multiple births may require an elective Caesarean ⬜

B A previous Caesarean section birth isn't a reason for an elective Caesarean ⬜

C Elective Caesareans take place before labour starts naturally ⬜

D Severe bleeding from the uterus is a reason for an elective Caesarean ⬜

E An epidural anaesthetic is used in an elective Caesarean ⬜

F An epidural anaesthetic makes the mother unconscious ⬜

G An elective Caesarean may be used if the baby is in the wrong position ⬜

H An elective Caesarean will be chosen for an HIV positive mother ⬜

4 Circle the correct option in the following sentences.

a) For an emergency Caesarean section a **local / general** anaesthetic sometimes is used.

b) A reason for an emergency Caesarean section is if progress in labour has **started / stopped**.

c) Foetal distress shown by the baby passing meconium **isn't / is** a reason for an emergency Caesarean.

d) **Severe / Slight** bleeding from the uterus is a reason for an emergency Caesarean.

Special Care for Babies

SCBUs and NICUs

1 What does SCBU and NICU stand for?

....

....

2 How long do babies spend in SCBUs?

....

....

....

Which Babies Need Special Care?

3 Which of the following babies need special care? Tick the correct options.

   A   Babies who are premature   ◯

   B   Babies with older mothers   ◯

   C   Babies with medical problems   ◯

   D   Babies with breathing difficulties   ◯

   E   Babies born to drug-addicted mothers   ◯

   F   Babies who are shocked after a difficult delivery   ◯

   G   Babies with a fontanelle   ◯

   H   Babies with a mother who has diabetes   ◯

Specialist Equipment in a SCBU

4 Circle the correct option in the following sentences.

   a)   An incubator keeps babies **incubated / isolated** from infection.

   b)   Light therapy is used to treat **spots / jaundice**.

   c)   A ventilator helps babies **feed / breathe**.

   d)   A nasogastric tube is used if babies have a(n) **mature / immature** sucking and swallowing reflex.

   e)   An intravenous line passes **fluids / solids** into babies.

   f)   A monitor checks **oxygen concentration / digestion**.

Premature Babies

1 Choose the correct words from the options given to complete the following sentences.

| 2.5kg | more | full | premature | developmental | 37 | medical |

_____ babies are born before _____ term

(_____ weeks). They weigh less than _____ / 5lbs at birth.

The earlier a baby arrives the _____ likely it is to need _____

help or have _____ delay in later life.

2 Which of the following are characteristics of premature babies? Tick the correct options.

A Inability to regulate body temperature ⬭

B Enlarged umbilical cord ⬭

C Weak immune system ⬭

D Inability to suck and swallow ⬭

E Low calcium, iron and blood sugar levels ⬭

F Small head ⬭

G Under developed lungs ⬭

H Low birth weight and little body fat ⬭

Bonding

3 Fill in the missing words to complete the following sentence.

Bonding is the feelings of _____ and affection between _____ and

_____ .

4 Circle the correct option in the following sentences.

a) Parents of premature babies may feel that the baby **doesn't / does** belong to them.

b) Skin-to-skin contact is also known as **kangaroo / koala** cuddling.

c) Parents **can / can't** provide some physical care for premature babies.

d) Parents **should / shouldn't** make eye contact with premature babies.

Newborn Babies

Physical Characteristics

1 Fill in the missing words on the diagram of a newborn baby.

A _____ – average of 50 cm

B _____ – after 7-10 days it shrivels and drops off

C _____ – full term is approximately 3.5 kg (low birth _____ is less than 2.5kg)

Comparatively **D** _____ head and tummy, and short **E** _____

F _____ – may have milia (small white / yellow spots), vernix, lanugo and birthmarks

G _____ – a tough membrane that protects the brain until the skull bones join together

H _____ – newborn white skinned babies have blue / grey ones; dark skinned babies have brown ones

Reflex Actions and Senses

2 Circle the correct option in the following sentences.

a) Newborn babies **can / can't** recognise the smell of their mother's milk.

b) Newborn babies **can / can't** show dislike for some tastes.

c) Newborn babies focus best at a distance of **15 / 20** cm.

d) Newborn babies **can't / can** recognise their mother's voice.

Apgar Test

3 Fill in the missing words to complete the following sentences.

At 1–5 _____ after birth, the _____ of newborn babies is checked

using the Apgar score. Most babies score _____ or above out of

_____. A score of less than _____ indicates that

_____ is needed.

The Post-natal Period

Checks After Birth

1 Which of the following statements are correct? Tick the correct options.

A   Six weeks after birth, a baby's fontanelle is checked ☐

B   Within 24 hours of birth, a baby's hips are checked for congenital dislocation ☐

C   Seven to ten days after birth, a baby's temperature is checked ☐

D   The emotional state of the mother is checked at the post-natal appointment ☐

E   Within seven to ten days, the NBSSC (newborn blood spot screening) is done ☐

F   At birth a baby's weight, length and head circumference are checked ☐

G   At the post-natal appointment, the size of the uterus is checked ☐

H   A baby's hearing is tested within 24 hours of birth ☐

Post-natal Depression

2 What three things can cause baby blues?

a) ....

b) ....

c) ....

3 Which of the following statements **isn't** correct? Tick the correct option.

A   Post-natal depression makes a mother feel overwhelmed and unable to cope ☐

B   Post-natal depression is another name for baby blues ☐

C   A severe case of post-natal depression may need hospitalisation ☐

D   Post-natal depression is an illness ☐

The Father's Role

4 Fill in the missing words to complete the following sentences.

Fathers are entitled to .... weeks paternity leave, which must be taken within

.... weeks of the baby's birth. Fathers receive ....

.... (SPP).

☐

Nutrition

Nutrients

1 Which of the following nutrients are macro nutrients? Tick the correct options.

A Starchy foods ⬜

B Calcium ⬜

C Iron ⬜

D Fat ⬜

E Sugar ⬜

F Vitamin A ⬜

G Protein ⬜

H Fluoride ⬜

2 Circle the correct option in the following sentences.

a) Fat is needed for **warmth / repair**.

b) Carbohydrates are sugar, starch and **fluoride / fibre**.

c) Protein is needed for **repair / calcium absorption**.

d) Carbohydrates provide **energy / Vitamin D**.

3 Why should a balanced diet be eaten every day?

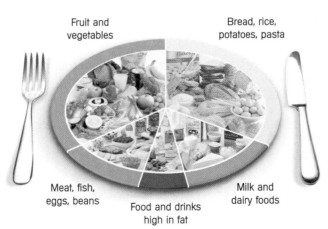

Fruit and vegetables

Bread, rice, potatoes, pasta

Meat, fish, eggs, beans

Food and drinks high in fat

Milk and dairy foods

....

....

4 Which vitamin is needed to help calcium absorption?

....

Obesity

1 Explain why the government has introduced legislation to control the advertising of some foods that are targeted at children.

....

....

2 Choose the correct words from the options given to complete the following sentences.

| **nutrients** | **junk** | **avoided** | **salt** |

_____ food, which may have a high fat, _____ or sugar content,

but contains few, if any, _____, should be _____ .

Obesity Problems

3 Children who are obese are more at risk of which of the following? Tick the correct options.

A Allergies

B Coronary heart disease (CHD)

C Genetic disorders

D Infections

E High blood pressure

F Hyperactivity

G Shortness of breath

H Type 2 diabetes

Food Allergies and Intolerance

4 Circle the correct option in the following sentences.

a) Children can be **insensitive / intolerant** to eggs.

b) A person who can't eat **wheat / dairy products** is a coeliac.

c) **Hyperactivity / Hypersensitivity** has been linked to tartrazine intolerance.

d) People who are lactose intolerant should drink **full fat / soya** milk.

e) **Food intolerance / Food allergies** can result in death in severe cases.

f) An **allergy / intolerance** may be outgrown.

Breastfeeding

Breastfeeding

1 Who can mothers turn to for help when they are breastfeeding?

_____

_____

Advantages for Mum and Baby

2 Which of the following are advantages of breastfeeding for the mother? Tick the correct options.

A It helps the mother's uterus to return to its previous size ☐

B It prevents the mother experiencing constipation ☐

C There are no bottles to prepare ☐

D It helps the mother regain her figure faster ☐

E It protects the mother from infection ☐

F It helps bonding with the baby ☐

G It's convenient ☐

H It's free ☐

3 Circle the correct option in the following sentences.

a) Breast milk contains **saturated / polyunsaturated** fatty acids for brain development.

b) Breast milk is **difficult / easy** to digest.

c) Breast milk contains **all / most** of the nutrients a newborn baby needs.

d) Breastfeeding reduces the likelihood of **enzymes / eczema**.

Potential Problems

4 What potential problems can be associated with breastfeeding?

_____

_____

_____

Bottle Feeding

1 Choose the correct words from the options given to complete the following sentences.

vitamins	**bottle**	**protection**	**formula milk**	**breast**

Special _____ _____ (modified cows' milk) can be given from

a _____. It contains all the _____ and minerals a baby needs, but

doesn't give the same _____ from infection as _____ milk.

Sterilisation

2 Fill in the missing words to complete the following sentence.

All equipment for feeding must be carefully _____, as milk is a breeding ground for

_____.

3 What are the two main methods of sterilising feeding equipment?

a) _____

b) _____

Bottle Feeding Safely

4 Which of the following statements are true about bottle feeding? Tick the correct options.

A Don't use damaged bottles and teats

B Throw the feed away after one hour

C Check the temperature of the milk before feeding the baby

D Follow the manufacturer's instructions when measuring powder

E Use a microwave to heat a feed

F Wash, rinse and sterilise equipment

G Make up formula milk with boiling hot water

H Keep reheating the feed until the baby has drunk it all

Weaning

Weaning

1 Choose the correct words from the options given to complete the following sentences.

seventeen weeks　　　　　　　　**six months**　　　　　　　　**recommends**

The Department of Health _____ starting weaning at _____

_____. It shouldn't be done before _____

_____.

Getting Started

2 Circle the correct options in the following sentences.

a) Babies are ready to wean when they still seem hungry after **puréed / milk** feeds.

b) Weaning too early can cause **allergies / antibodies**.

c) If babies demand food more often, they **shouldn't / should** be weaned.

d) Excess weight gain can be caused by weaning too **late / early**.

Stage 1 (6–7 Months)

3 Which of the following statements are true about Stage 1 of the weaning process? Tick the correct options.

A Serve the food chilled ◯

B Purée food using a blender ◯

C Only give foods containing gluten ◯

D Give food with small lumps in it ◯

E Use sterile equipment ◯

F Encourage a baby to eat by smiling and talking ◯

G Introduce a variety of tastes ◯

H Offer food in small amounts ◯

4 What should you do if a baby refuses a new food?

_____

_____

Stage 2 (7–9 Months)

1 Explain what is meant by the term 'finger foods'?

....

....

2 Circle the correct option in the following sentences about Stage 2 of the weaning process.

a) Introduce **breakfast / wheat-based** cereals.

b) Offer **soft / hard** foods to promote healthy teeth.

c) Use a **glass / beaker** to offer water to drink.

d) An example of a finger food is **toast / yoghurt**.

Stage 3 (9–12 Months)

3 Fill in the missing words to complete the following sentences.

By Stage .... of weaning, babies can eat the .... food as the

family, ... times a day. Food should be .... or

.... if it can't be eaten with fingers.

4 Which of the following statements are true about Stage 3 of the weaning process? Tick the correct options.

A Babies need healthy snacks and drinks between meals ⬭

B Babies are unwilling to try new textures ⬭

C After 12 months the milk feed is for nutrition, not comfort ⬭

D The amount of milk that babies drink decreases ⬭

E Babies of this age have small stomachs ⬭

F At 9 months full fat milk can be given ⬭

G The amount of solid food that babies eat increases ⬭

H Babies are willing to try new flavours ⬭

Children and Food

Types of Food Used for Weaning

1 Circle the correct options in the following sentences.

a) Commercially prepared food is **difficult / easy** to prepare.

b) There's less possibility of fussy eating if **home made / commercially prepared** food is used.

c) The ingredients can be more varied in **commercially prepared / home made** food.

d) Portion size is easier to control in **home made / commercially prepared** food.

2 Explain what is meant by 'organic food'.

....

....

Food Refusal

3 Food refusal is common between which ages?

....

Developing Healthy Eating Habits

4 Which of the following are good ways of developing healthy eating habits? Tick the correct options.

A	Help a child by feeding them	◯
B	Serve small portions	◯
C	Use food as a reward	◯
D	Make food look attractive	◯
E	Let children help to prepare a meal	◯
F	Make children eat everything on their plate	◯
G	Get cross if a child won't eat	◯
H	Eat together as a family	◯

Food Poisoning

Causes and Symptoms

1 Fill in the missing words to complete the following sentence.

Food poisoning is caused by harmful bacteria, such as .... ,

.... and ....

Preventing Food Poisoning

2 Circle the correct options in the following sentences.

a) Keep the fridge temperature between **-1−4°C / 1−4°C**.

b) Follow the **storage / packaging** instructions on food labels.

c) **Do / don't** lick fingers or bowls.

d) Wash hands **quickly / thoroughly**.

3 Which of the following statements show good practice in the kitchen? Tick the correct options.

A   To prevent waste, keep any leftover reheated food

B   Empty rubbish bins once a week

C   Use antibacterial cleaners on work surfaces

D   Avoid cross contamination (transfer of bacteria) by keeping raw and cooked food apart

E   Clean equipment thoroughly with hot soapy water

F   Keep food on a work surface

G   Sterilise babies' feeding equipment

H   Reheat foods correctly

4 What rules should you apply to pets and the kitchen?

....

....

Areas of Development

Areas of Development

1 The four areas of development are sometimes represented by the word PIES. What does PIES stand for?

....

2 Explain what is meant by 'growth'.

....

Milestones

3 Choose the correct words from the options given to complete the following sentences.

| **happen** | **achievements** | **guidelines** | **walking** | **master** |

Milestones are .... for when major .... will

...., e.g. when children .... a new skill, like

....

Intellectual Development

4 Which of the following statements are true? Tick the correct options.

A Intellectual development is about making friends

B Intellectual development includes reading and writing

C Intellectual development includes growth

D Intellectual development is the development of the mind / brain

E Intellectual development includes imagination

F Intellectual development includes running, jumping and skipping

G Intellectual development includes number skills

H Intellectual development is not linked with other areas of development

Concepts

5 Explain how the understanding of concepts takes place.

....

....

Intellectual Development

How do Children Learn?

1 Circle the correct option in the following sentences.

a) Children learn by **expertise / experience**.

b) Repetition and practice **doesn't / does** help children learn.

c) **Some / All** children learn through play.

d) Exploration **isn't / is** a way in which children learn.

How to Help Intellectual Development

2 Which of the following wouldn't help intellectual development? Tick the correct option.

A Providing suitable toys ⬜

B Encouragement, support, praise and quality time ⬜

C An unhealthy diet ⬜

D Visiting new places ⬜

3 Which of the following activities would stimulate intellectual development in an 18 month old child? Tick the correct options.

A Visiting the theatre ⬜

B Make believe games ⬜

C 'Feely' bag ⬜

D Baking ⬜

E Action games ⬜

F Musical statues ⬜

G Songs ⬜

H Making musical instruments ⬜

4 How does changing a three month old baby's position help intellectual development?

_____

Writing and Drawing

Writing and Drawing

1 Choose the correct words from the options given to complete the following sentences.

drawing   **scribbled**   **end result**   **experiment**   **experience**   **materials**

Children need a range of .... and large sheets of paper to let them

.... A .... isn't always produced. Sometimes a picture is

.... over because the .... is more important than the

.... , ...

2 Match the pictures **A–E** with the correct age group **1–5**. Enter the appropriate number in the box provided.

A ◯   **B** ◯   **C** ◯   **D** ◯   **E** ◯

1 5–6 years   **2** 15 months

3 2–3 years   **4** 18 months

5 4 years

3 Which of the following writing and drawing skills would you expect from a 4 year old? Tick the correct options.

A Scribbling to and fro ◯   **B** Able to copy OX ◯

C Primitive tripod grasp ◯   **D** Able to trace over words ◯

E Pictures with background details ◯   **F** Figures have a head, body, legs and arms ◯

G Holding a pencil well ◯   **H** Able to colour inside lines ◯

4 What can children express through drawing?

....

Speech and Language Development

1 Explain the difference between the pre-linguistic and linguistic stages of speech and language development.

....

....

2 Circle the correct options in the following sentences.

a) Echolalia is present at **12 / 6** months.

b) Telegraphic speech is used at **1 / 2** years.

c) Gurgling happens at **9 months / 5–6 weeks**.

d) Holophrases are used at **3 / 1** year(s).

3 Which of the following statements apply to a 2–3 year old child? Tick the correct options.

A Is understood outside the family ⬭

B Uses 6–40 identifiable words ⬭

C Uses incorrect word endings ⬭

D Uses 'I', 'me', 'you' correctly ⬭

E Has a vocabulary of 2000+ words ⬭

F Asks 'why?', 'what?', 'who?' ⬭

G Uses crucial words ⬭

H Uses complex sentences ⬭

Encouraging Speech

4 Choose the correct words from the options given to complete the following sentences.

interrupting   **open**   **verbal**   **time**

You can encourage speech by constant .... interaction, not

.... or laughing at mistakes, using .... questions, and giving

children .... to speak.

Physical Development

What is Physical Development?

1 Explain the difference between gross motor skills and fine motor skills.

....

....

....

2 Fill in the missing words to complete the following sentence.

Sensory development relates to ...., hearing, ...,

...., and ....

Milestones 0–1 Year

3 Which of the following milestones will a baby reach by the age of 12 months? Tick the correct options.

A No head control ◯

B Primitive tripod grip ◯

C Reflexes, e.g. Moro reflex ◯

D Deliberately throws objects ◯

E Walks with one hand held ◯

F Legs bear weight when held upright ◯

G Focuses on distant objects ◯

H 'Cruises' with feet wide apart ◯

4 Choose the correct ages from the options given to complete the following sentences. The ages may be used more than once.

9 months   **1 month**   **6 months**

a) At ...., a baby starts to support its head and chest with straight arms.

b) At ...., a baby starts to use the inferior pincer grip.

c) At ...., a baby starts to track objects.

d) At ...., a baby starts to use the palmar grasp to pass objects from hand to hand. ◯

Collins Revision

GCSE Child
Development
ESSENTIALS

GCSE

Child Development

Workbook Answers

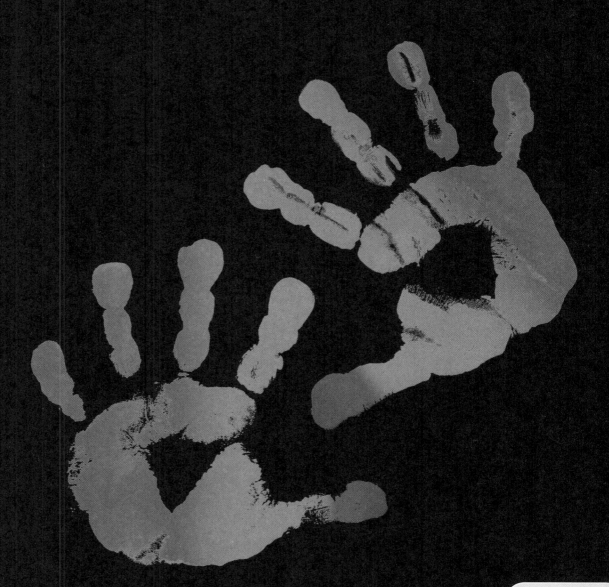

Formerly LONSDALE

GCSE Child Development
Workbook Answers

Page 4

1. A; C; D; G

2. People living together.

3. Primary socialisation is when parents teach children what is expected of them. Secondary socialisation is the influence of wider society, e.g. the media.

4. a) nuclear
b) sometimes
c) can

5. shared care, two, both, joint.

Page 5

1. Looked after children are looked after by, or in the care of, the local authority through social services.

2. C; E; F; G

3. C

4. Residential, short-term, exception, severe.

Page 6

1. a) more
b) simpler
c) more

2. nature, environment.

3. B; E; F; H

4. Culture is behaviour learned both from the family and society.

5. multicultural, ethnic groups, culture.

Page 7

1. A; C; E; H

2. Accept any sensible answer, for example: children can bring joy and pride, satisfaction from raising them, and love.

3. True.

4. a) bad
b) bad
c) good
d) bad

5. This phrase means that you think you are getting too old to wait to have children.

Page 8

1. a) age
b) sometimes
c) religious beliefs
d) can

2. Pregnancy, sterilisation, cutting, women, vasectomy.

3. a)–b) In any order: the morning after pill, fitting an IUD.

4. NFP methods work by identifying times in the menstrual cycle when a woman is most fertile and not having sexual intercourse at these times.

5. A; C; E; F.

Page 9

1. C; F; G

2. A male condom may split / be torn, damaged, come off or not be put on correctly.

3. a) are
b) no
c) isn't
d) does

4. oestrogen / progestogen, progestogen / oestrogen, mini.

5. a)–c) In any order: diaphragm, intrauterine device (IUD), intrauterine system (IUS).

Page 10

1. a) urethra
b) foreskin
c) prostate gland
d) scrotum

2. B; D; F; H

3. sperm, epididymis, ejaculation, ducts, prostate gland / seminal vesicles, seminal vesicles / prostate gland, fluid.

4. Sperm need seminal fluid for nourishment.

Page 11

1. a) is
b) can't
c) deteriorates
d) puberty

2. B; E; F; H

3. The uterus is a pear-shaped organ about the size of a clenched fist, with very muscular walls.

4. A5; B4; C3; D2; E1

Page 12

1. A healthy lifestyle.

2. A; C; F; G; H

3. folic acid, three months, spina bifida, green, wholegrain.

4. C

Page 13

1. dominant, weak.

2. a) weak
b) are
c) 23
d) do

3. a) two
b) abnormal
c) closely
d) inherited

4. A; F; G; H

Page 14

1. C

2. urine sample, gonadotrophin.

3. a) estimated delivery date
b) 280 days
c) 37–42
d) early dating scan

4. E; F; G

Page 15

1. one, uterus, naturally, likely, fertility.

2. a) Twins
b) Triplets
c) Quadruplets
d) Quintuplets
e) Sextuplets

3. B; D; F; H

4. a) often
  b) premature
  c) increased
  d) increases

Page 16

1. C

2. a) FAS
  b) mental impairment
  c) SIDS
  d) hard

3.

Foods to Avoid	Problem	Effect
Eggs, unless hard boiled; products containing raw egg	**Salmonella**	Food poisoning
Unpasteurised milk; incorrectly reheated cook-chill food	Listeriosis	**Miscarriage, still birth, severe illness**
Liver and liver products	Vitamin A	Too much harms the baby
Undercooked meat	Toxoplasmosis	Miscarriage; still birth; blind baby
Coffee	**Caffeine**	Miscarriage; low birth weight

4. A; C; D

Page 17

1.

Cause	Problem
Blocked fallopian tube / thick cervical mucus	Sperm can't reach the egg
No ovulation / hormone imbalance	**No egg**
Insufficient sperm / poor quality	Egg won't be fertilised

2. specialist, diseases, reproductive.

3. hormone, surgically, test tube, eight, uterus, fallopian tube.

4. B; D; F; G

Page 18

1. a) 1–3 months
  b) 4–6 months
  c) 7–9 months

2. B

3. a) can
  b) can't
  c) has
  d) closed.

4. Vernix is a white greasy substance that protects the baby's skin, and lanugo is fine hair that keeps the foetus warm.

5. A3; B2; C5; D6; E4; F1

Page 19

1. a) is
  b) is
  c) is
  d) 500g

2. B; D; G; H

3. sac, fluid, 37°C, cushions, bangs.

4. The umbilical cord is clamped in two places and cut between the clamps.

Page 20

1. A; B; D; E; F

2. A foetal heartbeat can be checked using a sonic aid or pinard stethoscope.

3. A; D; E; G

4. confirms, exact, size, number, heartbeat, cord, position.

Page 21

1. A; B; D; G

2. amniocentesis, 15–19, amniotic, ultrasound, needle, uterus.

3. a)–d) Any four from: the sex of the baby; viral infections; the baby's lung development; spina bifida; genetic conditions such as Down's syndrome or Edwards' syndrome

4. Chorionic villus sampling (CVS).

Page 22

1. a) straightforward
  b) may
  c) routine
  d) ante-natal

2. A community midwife works as part of a community team, and a maternity unit midwife works in a hospital.

3. A; C

4. B

5. a) home
  b) invaluable
  c) ante-natal
  d) EDD

Page 23

1. a) last
  b) midwives
  c) are
  d) don't

2. a)–c) Any three from: attend all scans, read up on pregnancy and childbirth, go to ante-natal classes, provide emotional support, offer practical help, e.g. with housework.

3. A woman records her ideas and expectations of birth on a written birth plan.

4. C; E; F; G; H

Page 24

1. C; D; E; F; G

2. midwife, temperature, protective, birthing pool.

3. B

4. a) one month
  b) resuscitating

Page 25

1. A; D; F; G

2. Hotel rooms.

3. a) relax
  b) double
  c) low
  d) sometimes

4. midwife, hospital, complications, mother, six.

Page 26

1. In the lower part of the spine.

2. B

3. drug, injected, muscle, bottom, drowsy, placenta, control.

4. B; E; F; G; H

Page 27

1. B

2. birthing pool, bath, 37°C, pain, hospital.

3. a)–c) Any three from: breathing and massage, acupuncture, homeopathy, aromatherapy, reflexology.

4. disadvantages, may not, qualified.

Page 28

1. birth, hormones, mother, uterus, cervix, baby.

2. A; C; D; F; H

3. The amniotic fluid is clear or slightly pink.

4. amniotic fluid, vagina, amniotic, trickle, gush.

Page 29

1. An episiotomy is a cut made in the vagina.

2. C

3. a) strong; canal
b) gradually
c) widest; vagina.

4. injection, bleeding, placenta, contractions.

5. B

Page 30

1. C

2. a) breech
b) across
c) sometimes

3. B; C; E; G

4. Oxytocin

5. In a Ventouse delivery, a metal or plastic cup is attached to the baby's head by a vacuum. In a forceps delivery, forceps (curved metal blades) are applied to each side of the baby's head. In both cases, the baby is eased out when contractions occur.

Page 31

1. operation, abdominal, uterus, bikini, removed.

2. a)–b) In any order: elective, emergency.

3. A; C; E; G; H

4. a) general
b) stopped
c) is
d) severe

Page 32

1. SCBU stands for Special Care Baby Unit and NICU stands for Neonatal Intensive Care Unit.

2. Babies can spend anything from a few hours up to several months in an SCBU.

3. A; C; D; E; F; H

4. a) isolated
b) jaundice
c) breathe
d) immature
e) fluids
f) oxygen concentration

Page 33

1. premature, full, 37, 2.5kg, more, medical, developmental.

2. A; C; D; E; G; H

3. Love, parent / child, child / parent

4. a) doesn't
b) kangaroo
c) can
d) should

Page 34

1. A length
B umbilical cord
C weight
D large
E legs
F skin
G fontanelle
H eyes

2. a) can
b) can
c) 20
d) can

3. minutes, condition, 7, 10, 7, help.

Page 35

1. B; D; E; F; G; H

2. a)–c) In any order: hormonal changes, lack of sleep, recovering from labour.

3. B

4. 2, 8, statutory paternity pay.

Page 36

1. A; D; E; G

2. a) warmth
b) fibre
c) repair
d) energy

3. A variety of foods should be eaten every day to ensure that you are eating a wide range of nutrients, and have a healthy diet.

4. Vitamin C or vitamin D.

Page 37

1. The government has introduced this legislation because some of these foods are high in calories, and eating lots of them can result in obesity.

2. junk, salt, nutrients, avoided.

3. B; D; E; G; H

4. a) intolerant
b) wheat
c) Hyperactivity
d) soya
e) Food allergies
f) intolerance

Page 38

1. Help is available from midwives, health visitors and support groups, e.g. the NCT and La Leche League.

2. A; C; D; F; G; H

3. a) polyunsaturated
b) easy
c) all
d) eczema

4. In any order: embarrassment, breastfeeding can be tiring, not enough milk is produced, it can be difficult to return to work or go out, sore or inverted nipples.

Page 39

1. formula milk, bottle, vitamins, protection, breast.

2. sterilised, bacteria.

3. a)–b) **In any order:** steam sterilisation; cold water / chemical sterilisation.

4. A; B; C; D; F

Page 40

1. recommends, six months, seventeen weeks.

2. **a)** milk
   b) allergies
   c) should
   d) early

3. B; E; F; G; H

4. You should try the food again later, or mix it with a food that you know the baby does like.

Page 41

1. Finger foods are foods that babies can eat on their own, with supervision, by holding them in their hands.

2. **a)** wheat-based
   b) hard
   c) beaker
   d) toast

3. 3, same, 3, mashed / chopped, chopped / mashed.

4. A; D; E; G; H

Page 42

1. **a)** easy
   b) home made
   c) home made
   d) home made

2. Organic food doesn't contain chemicals, fungicides, pesticides or synthetic drugs.

3. 9 months to 4 years.

4. B; D; E; H

Page 43

1. **Any three from:** salmonella, E-coli, listeria monocytogenes, bacillus cereus, staphylococcus aureus.

2. **a)** 1–4°C
   b) storage
   c) don't
   d) thoroughly

3. C; D; E; G; H

4. Keep pets out of the kitchen, and use separate cutlery and bowls for them.

Page 44

1. PIES stands for physical, intellectual, emotional and social.

2. Growth is an increase in weight, size and height.

3. guidelines, achievements, happen, master, walking.

4. B; D; E; G

5. The understanding of concepts starts with general ideas and understanding of physical things that can be seen or felt, and progresses to abstract ideas, e.g. morals.

Page 45

1. **a)** experience
   b) does
   c) All
   d) is

2. C

3. C; E; G

4. It stimulates the senses and prevents boredom.

Page 46

1. materials, experiment, drawing, scribbled, experience, end result.

2. A5; B2; C4; D1; E3

3. B; D; F; G

4. They can express their ideas, thoughts and feelings, and use their imagination.

Page 47

1. In the pre-linguistic stage, communication is through sounds. In the linguistic stage, words are simple holophrases, then complex sentences.

2. **a)** 6
   b) 2
   c) 5–6 weeks
   d) 1

3. A; C; D; F

4. verbal, interrupting, open, time.

Page 48

1. Gross motor skills are the use and control of large muscles. Fine motor skills are the use and control of the hands and fingers.

2. **In any order:** sight, touch, taste, smell.

3. B; D; E; G; H

4. **a)** 6 months
   b) 9 months
   c) 1 month
   d) 6 months.

Page 49

1. independently, arms, upstairs, backwards.

2. C

3. **a)** 2
   b) 2 years
   c) 6–8
   d) wrists

4. B; C; E; G; H

Page 50

1. Children have to learn to recognise and control their emotions so that they can behave in a socially acceptable way.

2.

Age	Stage of Emotional Development
2 years	Very egocentric
3 years	May develop fears, e.g. of the dark
12 months	Shy with strangers
4 years	Sense of humour
5 years	Happy to leave parents for longer
15 months	Rapid mood swings

3. common, tired, seeking, E, not.

4. naughty; Don't; Cuddle; patient.

Page 51

1. independence, choices, avoiding, defiance, independent, expectations.

2. a) praise
   b) confident
   c) consistent
   d) not laughing

3. A; B; D; E; G

4. Regression is when a child temporarily goes back to an earlier stage of development.

5. B

Page 52

1. Social skills allow children to fit in with the people who live with and around them.

2. A; C; G

3. age, communicate, people / children.

4. C

Page 53

1. encouraged, reinforcing, encouraging, building.

2. Social isolation (having no friends).

3. A; C; D; E; G; H

4. In any order: age, ability, understanding.

5. B

Page 54

1. A; B; D; E; H

2. a) texture
   b) age
   c) should
   d) fabric

3. Bookstart is a national programme that provides free books for children at 7–9 months, 18–30 months and 3–4 years.

4. Educational, limited, adult, talked.

Page 55

1. Play is important because it lets a child make sense of the world and develop physically, intellectually, emotionally and socially.

2. Instinctively, structured, spontaneous, initiated, interference.

3. D

4.

Type of Play	Description
Parallel play	Children play alongside each other
Looking on play	Children just watch others
Joining in play	Children do the same activity in their own way

5. A; C; D

Page 56

1. They should be stored and used according to the instructions given. The use-by date should be checked.

2. a)–d) In any order: plasters; an eye bath; scissors; calamine lotion; bandages; tweezers; antiseptic wipes / cream; or any other sensible answer.

3. Accident, calm, reassure.

4. C; H

5. You should switch off the power and move the child away from the electricity source with a non-metal object.

Page 57

1. A parasite is an organism that lives on another organism, obtaining food from it.

2. C

3. A; C; E; H

4. C

Page 58

1. B

2.

Illness	How to Recognise
Chicken pox	Rash; small red patches develop into blisters, which turn crusty and fall off
Rubella	Mild cold; pink rash; pink spots that merge together
Meningitis	Headache; fever; stiff neck; aching joints; dislike of light; severe sleepiness; fine red / purple rash that doesn't fade under pressure
Whooping cough	Cold / cough that develops into exhausting coughing bouts, making breathing difficult
Mumps	Slight fever; earache; swollen gland in front of ears
Tuberculosis	Cough; fever (can mimic other diseases)
Measles	Cough / cold; sore watery eyes; red blotchy rash

3. a) mumps
   b) chicken pox
   c) Tuberculosis
   d) Meningitis

Page 59

1. a) encourage
   b) comfort them
   c) give
   d) lots of

2. a) Ear thermometer
   b) Digital thermometer
   c) Forehead thermometer

3. colour, less.

4. A; C; E; F; H

Page 60

1. a) Strange
   b) Unpleasant
   c) absent
   d) different

2. B; D; E; F; G; H

3. An emergency admission is not known about in advance. A pre-planned non-emergency admission is known about.

4. C

Page 61

1. a) 2 months
   b) serious
   c) do
   d) antibodies

2. A; D; E; F

3.

Vaccine	Protects Against
d / D	Diphtheria
P	Pertussis (whooping cough)
IPV	Polio
MMR	Measles, Mumps, Rubella (German Measles)
Hib	Haemophilus influenza type BC
MenC	Meningitis

Page 62

1. Newborns sleep for 16–20 hours a day, and feed about every 4 hours.

2. a) 4 months
b) 3
c) 6 months
d) do

3. growth, mentally.

4. A; B; C; E; G; H

Page 63

1. B

2. A; B; D; E; G; H

3. a) Vitamin D
b) sunblock
c) UV
d) regularly

4. Put the pram in the shade, and use a canopy or parasol.

Page 64

1. A; D; F; H

2. Crawling, shoes, walking.

3. C

4. a) reducing
b) aren't
c) easy
d) aren't

Page 65

1. A; B; D; F; H

2. a) good
b) should
c) sturdy
d) should

3. B

4. A guard or safety rails can be added to make beds safe for young children.

Page 66

1. B; C; D; E

2. a) 18°C–21°C
b) warm
c) never
d) front to back

3. A baby should be wrapped in a warm towel so that no body heat is lost.

4. kick, exercise.

Page 67

1. a) alcohol
b) sweets
c) plastic bags
d) scissors

2. A; C; E; F; G

3. A six month old baby might choke or suffocate because this is the age at which they put things into their mouths to explore them (mouthing).

4. a) Lion Mark
b) CE mark
c) Kitemark

Page 68

1. Cover, fire, install / fit, fit / install, protectors.

2. A; B; C; D; E; G

3. a) low
b) locked
c) should
d) regularly

4. Children should stand still and wait until they are found.

Page 69

1. restraints, EEC, replaced, immobilised, front.

2. A; B

3. A; B; C; F; H

4. correct, age, securely, unattended.

Page 70

1. The EYFS sets standards for all children from birth to five in development, learning and care.

2. inspections, parents and carers.

3. a) emotional
b) language
c) solving
d) understanding
e) physical
f) creative

4. A; D; F; H

Page 71

1. To encourage socialisation, to offer play opportunities, and to give parents a break.

2. A; C; F; G

3. a) often
b) can't
c) is
d) may

4. advantages, care, after.

Page 72

1. B

2. C; E; F; H

3. a) birth
b) can
c) usually
d) expensive

4. Au pairs can help children learn about another culture, they live in, they can work flexible hours, and help with household tasks.

Page 73

1. B; D; G; H

2. two, five.

3. B

4. a) 3–5
b) have
c) open
d) free

Page 74

1. special, health, learning.

2. a) extra
b) cystic fibrosis
c) an inherited gene
d) cerebral palsy

3. B; D; E; F

4. B

5. intellectual, early, academically, development, same.

Page 75

1. basic, severity, extra.

2. A; B; D; E; G; H

3. The positive effects are that the child with special needs can bring a family closer together (bonding), and help siblings to be more tolerant of one another.

4. D

Page 76

1. A; C; E; F; G

2. government, wide, integrated, community, professionals, parents, needs.

3. A 'means-tested benefit' isn't available to everyone. It depends on individual family circumstances, e.g. your income.

4. D

Page 77

1. a) growth
   b) post-natal
   c) baby clinics
   d) five

2. A; C; D; E; F; H

3. People may not know what benefits are available to them. They may be apathetic, embarrassed, want to keep their independence or unable to fill in the necessary forms.

4. B

Exam Style Questions
Page 78 – Section A

1. a) A family is the basic unit of society. It is a group of people living together, who are married, co-habit, or who are related by birth or adoption.

b) i)–iv) Accept any four of the following: parents are divorced; one parent has died; absent parent, e.g. working abroad or away from home, in prison, in hospital; surrogacy arrangement; adoption by single parent; birth to a single mum by choice; birth to a single mum as a result of a sexual attack.

c) Give yourself one mark for each of the following points:
   – A foster family provides long-term or short-term care. An adoptive family provides permanent care.
   – Foster parents are paid by social services to look after children. Adoptive parents aren't.
   – Children in foster care are supported by their foster family to maintain regular contact with their birth parents, with the aim of re-uniting the family. This doesn't happen in adoptive families.
   – Adoptive families have the same legal rights and responsibilities as birth parents. Foster families don't.
   – Adopted children usually take the name of their adoptive family. Foster children don't.
   – Adopted children from abroad may be placed in adoptive families. Fostered children don't come from abroad.

Page 79 – Section B

2. a) One mark for each of:
   A: fallopian tube
   B: ovary
   C: uterus
   D: ovum (egg)
   E: vagina
   F: funnel
   G: cervix

b) One mark for each of:
   i) ovaries
   ii) fallopian tube
   iii) lining of the uterus
   iv) in the uterus
c) 28 days
d) i)–ii) In any order: oestrogen, progesterone.

Page 80 – Section C

3. a) One mark for each of:
   A: testis
   B: scrotum
   C: sperm tube
   D: penis
   E: bladder
b) Testosterone
c) i) Boy / male
   ii) Girl / female
d) identical (monozygotic) twins.

Page 81 – Section D

4. a) The abdomen is covered in gel. A hand-held scanner is used to reflect sound waves, which project an image of the baby and its internal organs onto a screen.
b) i)–iii) Accept any three of the following: confirmation of pregnancy; exact foetal age and size; number of foetuses; abnormalities, e.g. of limbs and internal organs; heartbeat; umbilical cord; position of the placenta.
c) Breech
d) i) A fine plastic tube is placed in the lower part of the spine. Liquid anaesthetic is put into this.
   ii) It works by blocking the nerves that send messages to the brain.

iii) 1.–2. Accept any of the following: must be administered by an anaesthetist; can only be given in hospital; the mother doesn't know when to 'push', as she can't feel the contractions; doesn't relieve pain immediately; may cause headaches / backache after birth; may increase length of labour; may increase need for Ventouse / forceps delivery.

Page 82 – Section E

5. a) The advantages of a home birth are:
- The familiar surroundings make the mother relaxed.
- The midwife is more likely to be known.
- Privacy is guaranteed.
- There's no routine to follow, e.g. mealtimes.
- No transport is needed.
- More people can be present at the birth.
- There are no other babies crying to disturb the mother.
- Less disruption to other children in the family.

b) The circumstances are:
- A woman having a multiple birth.
- A woman in premature labour.
- A mother with a history of miscarriage.
- First / fourth or subsequent baby.
- A woman who has had previous Caesarean sections.
- A woman under 17 and over 35.
- A woman with medical problems, e.g. high blood pressure.
- A woman with unsuitable home conditions.
- A woman whose baby is in the breech position.

c) Bonding is the feelings of love and affection between a parent and a child.

d) i)–ii) In any order: they may be afraid to love the baby in case it dies; they may feel that the baby doesn't belong to them – it belongs to the hospital; they may be put off by the amount of complexity and equipment; they may have difficulties holding / handling the baby.

Page 83 – Section F

6. To gain full marks a detailed answer is needed, which covers the following points:

i) The muscles in the uterus gradually dilate (open up) the cervix 8–10cm. This is so the baby's head can pass through. Signs that labour has started include:
- A show, when the plug of mucus sealing the cervix comes away. It may be blood stained. It can go unnoticed by the mother.
- Contractions that are regular and strong, when the uterus becomes tight and then relaxes. They start at 30–40 minute intervals. They become stronger and closer together, which causes pain.
- Waters breaking (membrane rupture). This is when clear or slightly pink amniotic fluid comes out of the vagina when the amniotic sac bursts. It can be a slow trickle or a sudden gush. (The waters sometimes break in Stage 2 of labour.)
- Backache, nausea, vomiting and diarrhoea are common.

ii) The following takes place in Stage 2 of labour:
- Very strong contractions push the baby along the birth canal (which is formed by the uterus, cervix and vagina).
- The mother has an urge to push.
- The midwife gives guidance so that the head is born gradually. When the widest part of the head comes out of the vagina, it is known as crowning.
- Sometimes the head causes a small tear, which may or may not be stitched.
- Sometimes an episiotomy (a cut in the vagina) is needed to let the head pass through. This is stitched.
- After the head emerges, the body slides out quickly and easily.
- The baby may cry and breathe as the head emerges, or after the shoulders and body are pushed out.
- The umbilical cord is cut between two clamps. This doesn't hurt the baby.
- The baby is a separate person.

iii) In Stage 3 of labour, the placenta and remaining cord are delivered. Sometimes an injection of syntometrine is given to stop excessive bleeding, and help the placenta and cord to be delivered. It takes 5–15 minutes of contractions. The placenta is examined, and any necessary stitching is completed.

Page 84 – Section G

7. a) i)–ii) In any order: if it is born before full term (before 37 weeks); if it weighs less than 2.5kg (5 lbs) at birth.

b)

Specialist Equipment	What if Does
i) Ventilator	Provides oxygen in a controlled way
ii) Incubator	Keeps baby's body temperature constant
iii) Monitor	Checks breathing and heartbeat
iv) Light therapy	Treats jaundice
v) Nasogastric tube	Feeds directly into the stomach

c) i)–iv) Accept any four of the following: sucking and swallowing; rooting; walking / stepping; falling (Moro); the grasp reflex; the startle reflex; crawling; blinking; asymmetric tonic neck.

d) For full marks include:
At 1–5 minutes after birth, a baby's condition is checked and scored. Checks are made for pulse / heartbeat, breathing, movement, skin colour and reflexes. Most babies score 7 or more and are fine. A score of less than 7 indicates that the baby needs help.

Page 85 – Section H

8. a) Your answer should cover both diet and exercise.
Diet
- Don't let the child eat more calories than are needed to provide energy.
- Avoid foods that are high in sugar (e.g. cakes, biscuits, chocolate). Replace them with healthy alternatives, e.g. yoghurt, fruit and vegetables.
- Avoid foods that are high in fat, e.g. chips, crisps, fried foods. Replace them with low fat versions, alternative foods, or use a different cooking method, e.g. grilling.
- Don't use food as a reward.

Exercise
- Encourage physical activity by providing opportunities to play outdoors.
- Visit play parks and ball pools, go swimming, go to gymnastics classes, dancing classes, etc.
- Provide toys that encourage physical activity, e.g. bikes, scooters, skipping ropes, hoops.
- Walk rather than use the car when possible.

b) i)–iii) Accept any three of the following: coronary heart disease (CHD); high blood pressure; type 2 diabetes; problems with joints and bones; increased risk of infection; breathlessness.

c) Your answer should refer to social and emotional effects.
Social effects include having no friends, being teased by peers, and being bullied by peers.
Emotional effects are feeling self conscious, embarrassed (especially in physical activities or PE), and having low self-esteem.

d) For full marks include: An allergy is much more serious than an intolerance. An allergy can result in a severe reaction or even death. An intolerance may be outgrown. Examples of intolerances might be eggs, lactose, dairy products. Examples of allergies could be nuts, chemical additives, wheat.

Page 86 – Section I

9. a) i) 1.–3. Accept any of the following advantages:
breast milk contains the correct balance of nutrients; breast milk contains antibodies; breast milk contains polyunsaturated fatty acids for brain development; breast milk is easy to digest; there is less likelihood of the baby being constipated, having eczema or allergies, or being obese.

ii) 1.–3. Accept any of the following advantages for the mother: breastfeeding is free and convenient; breastfeeding helps bonding; breastfeeding means that there is no preparation or sterilisation; breastfeeding helps the mother regain her figure faster; breastfeeding helps

the mother's uterus return to its previous size.

b) i)–ii) Accept any of the following: midwives; health visitors; support groups, e.g. La Leche League, National Childbirth Trust (NCT).

c) i)–ii) Accept any of the following: mothers are advised not to breastfeed if they are: HIV positive or have AIDS; taking non-prescribed drugs or are dependent on them; taking cancer drugs or undergoing radiation treatment.
Mothers may also be advised not to breastfeed if they have had breast surgery or breast cancer.

d) i)–iv) Accept any of the following: wash hands before touching equipment; wash, rinse and sterilise all equipment; use the correct amount of cooled boiled water; use the correct amount of powder and follow the manufacturer's instructions; check the milk is at the right temperature; make a fresh feed each time and throw the feed away after an hour.

Page 87 – Section J

10. a) i) Weaning is the gradual introduction of food to babies, and the reduction of milk consumption.
ii) Six months.
iii) Weaning is necessary because after six months milk alone can't provide the correct amount of iron and other nutrients needed for growth and development.

b) To gain high marks, you must include advantages and disadvantages of both types of food in your answer.
Advantages of **commercially prepared** foods are that:
- They are convenient for travelling / in an emergency.

- They are easy to use and store.
- They contain adequate levels of nutrients (shown on the label).
- They are the correct consistency for different stages of weaning.
- They are hygienically produced.
- They are quick to prepare.
- There are different types available.
- Many of the foods are organic, so ingredients don't contain chemicals, fungicides, pesticides or synthetic drugs.
- Some foods have nutrients added, or are additive free.

Disadvantages of **commercially prepared** foods are that:
- They are expensive.
- They have a bland flavour.
- Some nutrients are removed by processing.
- The portion size is pre-determined.

Advantages of **home made** foods are that:
- Ingredients are fresh and more varied, with no additives (colouring, flavouring, preservatives).
- They are less expensive.
- There is less possibility of fussy eating.
- Portion size can be controlled.
- Food can be frozen.
- They have more flavour / are less bland.
- No nutrients are removed by manufacturing processes.

Disadvantages of **home made** foods are:
- The preparation time.
- That you need equipment, e.g. a blender.

c) Young children can be encouraged to develop healthy eating habits in the following ways:
- The family should all eat the same food at regular mealtimes.
- Encourage independent eating by giving children their own cutlery and crockery.
- Avoid confrontation. Try to avoid stress by not bribing or coaxing, forcing or threatening.
- Remove unwanted food without comment.
- Don't use food to comfort or reward.
- Serve small portions.
- Eat healthy balanced meals.
- Serve a variety of foods that have been cooked healthily.
- Make food look attractive.
- Let children shop and help cook, and sometimes choose the menu.

Page 88 – Section K

11. a) i)–iii) **Accept any of the following:** don't lick fingers or bowls; don't cough, sneeze or smoke over food; keep nails short and clean; wash hands thoroughly.

b) i)–iv) **Accept any of the following:** clean all equipment, cutlery, etc. with hot soapy water; sterilise babies' feeding equipment; clean work surfaces, sinks, etc. with antibacterial cleaner; ensure that all foods, especially cook-chill meals, are correctly heated; throw away any left over reheated food; empty the rubbish bin regularly; keep pets out, and use separate cutlery and bowls for them.

c) i)–iii) **Accept any of the following:** use sell-by and use by dates correctly; keep food covered; follow storage instructions on labels; keep the fridge temperature between 1–4°C, and the freezer at -18°C; avoid cross contamination (transfer of bacteria) by keeping raw and cooked food apart.

Page 89 – Section L

12. a) **Your answer should be detailed and include some of the following points:**
- Make sure that the discipline is appropriate for the age of the child and their understanding. An 18 month old can't understand what a 4 year old can.
- Don't have too many rules, so the child isn't confused and clearly understands what boundaries have been set, i.e. what is right and what is wrong.
- Be clear about expectations, e.g. listening to parents, following instructions.
- Consistency is important to avoid giving the child mixed messages. This applies to behaviour, e.g. always saying please and thank you to both parents.
- Deal with problems immediately, ensuring that the child understands what they are, and that any punishment is clearly linked to the bad behaviour.
- Avoid conflict in situations where you can't enforce a rule, and avoid idle threats, e.g. a child can't be made to go to sleep, but can be made to stay in bed.
- Use distraction techniques if you can see bad behaviour about to happen.

- Praise and reward good behaviour to reinforce it. Use treats such as a visit to the park, a story, a cuddle, a star chart, playing with the child.
- Provide a good role model so children know what is acceptable behaviour, including saying sorry if necessary.
- Never use physical punishment, e.g. smacking, as using fear encourages violence and aggression.
- Don't shout at children because this will exacerbate the situation. Remain calm and cool and quietly in control.
- Show disapproval by using a stern voice, avoiding eye contact, looking disinterested and avoiding body contact (unless safety is an issue).
- Always give the child a warning so that they can alter their behaviour, but follow through with any punishment you've said will be imposed, e.g. withdraw a toy or activity, time in a naughty spot for the child to consider what they have done.

b) **Your answer should include the following points:**
- Parents may not want their child to play outside because they are concerned about the child being abducted. Parents might feel that the area isn't safe because it is subject to vandalism or crime.
- Parents may be at work so are unable to supervise outside play.
- The garden may not be safe (you could give examples such as fenced in, pond in garden, etc.).

- The house might not have a garden (e.g. because it is terraced or is in a block of flats with no outside play space).
- The house could be situated on a road with busy traffic.
- The child could be affected by allergies, especially in summer, e.g. pollen.
- The child may not be able to play outdoors because of unsuitable weather conditions, e.g. fog, very cold weather, windy conditions.
- Parents may be worried that their child will be bullied or teased by older children, or that they might try to copy unsuitable activities, such as skateboarding.
- There may be no other children to play with in the locality.
- There may not be any local play facilities, such as swings, play parks, etc.
- The child may have special needs, which make it difficult for them to play outside. Give a suitable example here, e.g. a child who is blind.

Page 90 – Section M

13. a)

Age	Example
3 months	Babbles, says aa, oo, ddd, mmm
12–18 months	**Holophrases, uses 6–40 identifiable words**
2 years	Telegraphic speech
4–5 years	Any from: Talks fluently, complex sentences, few grammatical mistakes, good pronunciation and articulation, large vocabulary of 2000+ words

b) **Any three of the following:**
Parents can encourage speech development by…
- constant verbal interaction
- giving children time to speak and not finishing their sentences
- not interrupting
- not laughing at their mistakes

- using 'open' questions that need more than a 'yes' or 'no' answer.

c) Gross motor skills is the use and control of large muscles. Fine manipulative skills is the control and use of the hands and fingers.

d) i)–ii) **Accept any of the following:** pincer grip; fastening buttons; holding pencil; fastening shoes; doing jigsaw puzzles.

e) Developmental milestones are checked and assessed by health visitors. These checks show if children have mastered skills, such as walking, by a certain age. If they haven't, then intervention may be needed by other agencies to help their development.

Page 91 – Section N

14. a) In your answer, make sure you give different actions to be taken. The table below shows a range of examples. For each correct answer one mark will be allocated. Maximum 4 marks.

Reason for Crying	Action Taken to Stop Crying
Thirsty	Give water or milk
Hungry	Feed
Tired	Get to sleep
Bored	Play with baby
Lonely	Spend time with baby
Uncomfortable	Check clothing and change nappy
Ill / in pain	Treat or seek medical help
Too hot / cold	Alter clothing / bedding to adjust temperature

b) i) **1.–2. Accept any of the following:** it soothes child quickly; it can be taken anywhere; its use can be controlled by parents.

ii) **1.–2. Accept any of the following:** it may get lost and can't be replaced; it may get dirty.

c) i) 2 years.

ii) If a child has a temper tantrum, the parents / carers should keep calm, be patient, and not shout or smack. They should explain it's not acceptable behaviour, be consistent and not reward bad behaviour, ignore or distract, and be a good role model, use a naughty step, and cuddle the child after the tantrum.

Page 92 – Section O

15. a) Play lets children make sense of the world and develop physically, intellectually, emotionally and socially. Try to give one example for each of these four areas (PIES).

b) i) In parallel play, children play alongside each other, but not with each other. There is no interaction. Approximate age: 2 years.

ii) In looking-on play, children just watch others, but don't join in. Approximate age: 3 years.

iii) In co-operative play, children play together. Approximate age: 3+ years.

c) i)–iv) Your answer could be almost any 'safe' (i.e. not sharp or breakable) everyday object, e.g. empty boxes, cartons, plastic containers, pans, spoons, a sieve, curtains, hats, blanket, etc.
1 mark for each answer.

d) i)–ii) Accept any of the following: poor neurological development; violent, anti-social or aggressive behaviour; being unfit / obese.

Page 93 – Section P

16. a) i)–ii) Accept any of the following: fresh air improves appetite; fresh air promotes a good night's sleep; fresh air encourages development of supple muscles when using tricycles, pedal cars, balls, hoops, etc.; fresh air gives children space to play and to let off steam.

b) i)–iii) Accept any of the following: use sunblock or high sun protection factor products (15+); apply it regularly; reapply it after playing in water; wear a hat that covers the back of the neck; protect feet and shoulders; don't play in the sun when it's at its hottest; play in the shade; wear UV protective clothing.

c) Use the following points in your answer, giving examples where you can, e.g. running, climbing, riding a bike, scooter, etc. Exercise is important in childhood because it improves general health, strengthens muscles, especially heart and lung muscles, sets good patterns for future behaviour (e.g. active lifestyle, keeping fit), makes children feel good (improves self-esteem), gives children confidence in their abilities, strengthens bones, and reduces the risk of being overweight.

Page 94 – Section Q

17. a) i)–iii) Accept any of the following: lightweight, soft, non-irritant, and non flammable; appropriate for the weather / indoor temperature; easy to put on and remove, e.g. envelope neck opening, and easy to access for nappy changing; easy to wash / dry / iron; no ribbons or open weave, which might trap fingers.

b) i)–iv) Accept any of the following: lightweight; no inside seams; low heel; flexible; slip resistant soles; adjustable fastening; growing room.

c) Use as many points from the list below as you can.
- No washing is required; they are thrown away when used.
- They are absorbent, reducing the possibility of nappy rash.
- They are easy to use.
- They are available in different versions, e.g. boy / girl, day / night, pull ups.
- They come in different sizes, which ensures a good fit.
- They are useful for travelling / on holiday.

d) Describe how to top and tail in a logical way, using the points listed below.
- Have all equipment ready beforehand.
- Have a warm room (18–21 °C).
- Remove the baby's clothes, except for their vest and nappy.
- Wipe their face gently with cotton wool and warm water.
- Use a fresh piece for each eye to avoid cross infection.
- Wipe from the bridge of the nose outwards.
- Clean the creases in the neck where milk can gather.
- Clean the baby's hands.
- Remove the nappy and clean the genital area.
- Don't pull back a boy's foreskin to clean.
- Clean a baby girl from front to back to avoid infection from bacteria.
- Replace the nappy and dress the baby.

18. a) You should identify how burns and scalds are caused, and give examples of how each can be prevented.

Hot drinks – don't drink with a baby in your arms, don't leave a hot drink on the floor, don't leave a hot drink on a table with a cloth.

Matches / lighters – keep them out of reach of children, teach children about dangers of matches and lighters.

Fires – use fireguards with an approved safety label, don't leave garden bonfires smouldering.

Cookers – keep children out of the kitchen if possible (put a baby in a playpen), use cooker guards, put pans on the back burners, have pan handles facing inwards.

Iron – never leave it unattended, put it where children can't reach it while it is cooling.

Radiators – use radiator guards.

Bath – put cold water in first, cover the hot tap with a special guard or a face cloth.

b) i) The Lion Mark is used on toys to show that the product has reached British Toy Manufacturers' standards, and is safe to use.

ii) This label is used to advise purchasers of the suggested age range for the toy. It avoids the potential danger of a toy, e.g. of giving a baby a toy with small parts that could be swallowed.

19. a) i)–iii) Accept any of the following: they may have different views on some issues, e.g. discipline; it may lead to family conflict and make relationships strained; children have less exposure to childhood illnesses; there is less opportunity to socialise with other children; grandparents' homes may not be child proof (i.e. a safe environment); children may become too attached to grandparents; grandparents may find looking after children physically demanding.

b) This answer should relate to children and parents, and include the following points. Where possible, examples should be used to illustrate the points.
   - Childminders work flexible hours.
   - They are not as expensive as some other childcare options.
   - They are usually experienced / have childcare qualifications.
   - They are Ofsted registered.
   - They offer a homely environment.
   - They can form a close bond with the child.
   - They can pick up / drop off at nursery.
   - They can provide continuity of care for many years, e.g. when the child starts school.
   - There are often other children to play with.
   - Siblings can be kept together.
   - Visits can be made to parks, etc.
   - Routines can be adapted to suit a child's individual needs.

c) Ofsted is a government regulatory body. It monitors the work in the EYFS that is concerned with the learning and care of children from 0–5. Ofsted inspectors regularly check the work of childminders, pre-schools, nurseries, etc. They check that all six areas of the EYFS curriculum are being covered for 3–5 year olds. These areas are…
1. personal, social and emotional development
2. communication, language and literacy
3. problem solving, reasoning and numeracy
4. knowledge and understanding of the world
5. physical development
6. creative development.
Ofsted reports findings from inspections in writing to parents and carers, and these are available to the general public. Ofsted makes recommendations for improvements that must be acted upon in order for Ofsted registration to continue.

ACKNOWLEDGEMENTS

The author and publisher are grateful to the copyright holders for permission to use quoted materials and images.

Every effort has been made to trace copyright holders and obtain their permission for the use of copyright material. The authors and publishers will gladly receive information enabling them to rectify any error or omission in subsequent editions. All facts are correct at time of going to press.

Published by Collins
An imprint of HarperCollins*Publishers*
1 London Bridge Street
London SE1 9GF

British Library Cataloguing in Publication Data.

A CIP record of this book is available from the British Library.

Book concept and development: Helen Jacobs
Commissioning Editor: Rebecca Skinner
Authors: Judi Sunderland and Leann Cooke
Project Editor: Emma Rae
Cover Design: Paul Oates
Inside Concept Design: Helen Jacobs and Sarah Duxbury
Text Design and Layout: Dragon Digital
Artwork: Lonsdale

Physical Development

Milestones 1–5 Years

1 Fill in the missing words to complete the following sentences.

At 15 months a child walks _____, using _____ to balance.

He walks _____ forwards and downstairs _____.

2 Which of the following physical milestones can a 3 year old achieve? Tick the correct option.

A Skipping ◯

B Uses mature pincer grip ◯

C Throws ball over arm, and can catch a ball ◯

D Dresses and undresses independently ◯

3 Circle the correct options in the following sentences.

a) At 15 months a child can build a **2 / 4** brick tower.

b) At **18 months / 2 years**, a child starts potty training.

c) At 2 years, a child can build a **6–8 / 8–10** brick tower.

d) At 18 months, a child can control their **ankles / wrists**.

4 Which of the following statements are correct? Tick the correct options.

A Aged 15 months, a child uses their preferred hand ◯

B Aged 3, a child undresses and dresses with help ◯

C Aged 3, a child can pedal and steer toys ◯

D Aged 15 months, a child can thread beads ◯

E Aged 15 months, a child can use a cup and spoon ◯

F Aged 15 months, a child can kick a ball ◯

G Aged 4, a child can go up and down stairs like an adult ◯

H Aged 5, a child can dance rhythmically ◯

Emotional Development

1 Why do children have to learn to recognise and control their emotions?

_____

_____

Stages of Emotional Development

2 Choose the correct ages from the options given to complete the following chart. Use each age once only.

3 years   **15 months**   **2 years**   **4 years**   **5 years**   **12 months**

Age	Stage of Emotional Development
	Very egocentric
	May develop fears, e.g. of the dark
	Shy with strangers
	Sense of humour
	Happy to leave parents for longer
	Rapid mood swings

Temper Tantrums

3 Fill in the missing words to complete the following sentence.

Temper tantrums are more _____ when a child is over _____,

attention _____, jealous, reacting to colourings and _____

numbers, bored, _____ wanting to share, or unhappy.

4 Circle the correct options in the following sentences about what you should do to deal with temper tantrums.

Use a **naughty / reward** step. **Do / Don't** smack the child. **Cuddle / Punish** the child after a temper tantrum. Be very **cross / patient** with the child.

Helping Emotional Development

1 Choose the correct words from the options given to complete the following sentences.

avoiding	defiance	expectations	independence	choices	independent

Develop .... by giving children .... and

.... power struggles. Accept that .... and disobedience are

an integral part of becoming .... Have reasonable ....

2 Circle the correct options in the following sentences.

a) Build self-esteem by using **criticism / praise**.

b) Self-esteem makes children feel **concerned / confident** about themselves.

c) Discipline should be **constant / consistent**.

d) Self-esteem can be built by **laughing / not laughing** at children.

Negative Feelings

3 Which of the following situations could negatively affect emotional development? Tick the correct options.

A   Moving house ⬜

B   A new baby ⬜

C   Playing in the park ⬜

D   Starting nursery ⬜

E   Change of carer ⬜

F   Going to a party ⬜

G   Death of a relative / pet ⬜

H   Visiting a farm ⬜

4 Explain what is meant by 'regression'.

....

....

5 Which of the following **is not** a way of expressing sibling rivalry? Tick the correct option.

A   Aggression ⬜   B   Co-operation ⬜

C   Withdrawal ⬜   D   Regression ⬜

Social Development

Social Skills

1 What do social skills allow children to do?

_____

_____

2 Which of the following **are not** social skills? Tick the correct options.

A Painting ◯

B Understanding rules ◯

C Understanding the concept of time ◯

D Respecting the ideas and feelings of others ◯

E Having standards of hygiene ◯

F Negotiating ◯

G Solitary play ◯

H Taking turns ◯

Social Experiences

3 Fill in the missing words to complete the following sentences.

Social experiences should be appropriate to the child's _____, and provide the

opportunity to mix and _____ with other _____.

Stages of Social Development

4 Which of the following statements **would not** apply to a six month old baby? Tick the correct option.

A Shy with strangers ◯

B Uses fingers to feed ◯

C Understands basic commands ◯

D Reacts differently to cross and pleasant voices ◯

Social Development

Encouraging Social Skills

1 Choose the correct words from the options given to complete the following sentences.

encouraging   **reinforcing**   **building**   **encouraged**

Social skills can be _____ by _____ acceptable behaviour,

by _____ independence, and by _____ self-esteem.

Negative / Anti-social Behaviour

2 What could be the effect on a child who behaves in a negative and anti-social way?

_____

3 Which of the following are examples of anti-social behaviour? Tick the correct options.

- **A** Self-harm, e.g. head banging ◯
- **B** Using good manners ◯
- **C** Temper tantrums ◯
- **D** Aggression, e.g. kicking, biting ◯
- **E** Seeking attention, e.g. refusing to co-operate ◯
- **F** Co-operative play ◯
- **G** Bullying and teasing ◯
- **H** Lying ◯

Discipline

4 Fill in the missing words to complete the following sentence.

Discipline should be appropriate for a child's _____ , _____

and _____ .

5 Which of the following is a good way of showing approval? Tick the correct option.

- **A** Looking disinterested ◯
- **B** Touching ◯
- **C** Not making eye contact ◯
- **D** Using a stern voice ◯

Toys, Books and TV

Toys

1 Which of the following should you check when you're buying toys? Tick the correct options.

A That they are washable (if for a baby) ⬭

B That they are strong and stable, with no sharp edges ⬭

C That they are cheap in a sale ⬭

D That they are non-toxic and lead free ⬭

E That they have a safety label, e.g. Lion Mark ⬭

F That they are advertised on TV ⬭

G That they are only suitable for boys or girls ⬭

H That they are suitable for the child's age and ability ⬭

Books and TV

2 Circle the correct options in the following sentences.

a) An example of a special feature in a book is **print size / texture**.

b) Books should be suitable for a child's **age / sex**.

c) Illustrations in books **should / shouldn't** be colourful.

d) Books can be made from **wool / fabric**.

3 What does Bookstart do?

....

....

4 Choose the correct words from the options given to complete the following sentences.

talked	**adult**	**educational**	**limited**

TV, DVDs and videos should have a good .... context and be watched for a

.... time, with an .... Programmes should be

.... about afterwards.

Play

1 Explain why play is important.

....

2 Choose the correct words from the options given to complete the following sentences.

spontaneous   **structured**   **interference**   **instinctively**   **initiated**

Children play ...., ... play is organised by others.

.... play happens on the spur of the moment, is ....

(started) by the child, and there is no adult ....

3 Which of the following **is not** a possible consequence of play malnourishment? Tick the correct option.

A   Poor neurological development   ◯

B   Being unfit and obese   ◯

C   Being more violent, anti-social and aggressive   ◯

D   Being more susceptible to infections   ◯

Stages of Play

4 Fill in the missing words to complete the following chart.

Type of Play	Description
	Children play alongside each other
	Children just watch others
	Children do the same activity in their own way

Types of Play

5 Which of the following statements are correct? Tick the correct options.

A   Riding a bike is an example of physical play   ◯

B   Manipulative play helps children to share and take turns   ◯

C   Imaginative play is also called pretend play   ◯

D   In creative play, children use their imaginations   ◯

Health and Safety

First Aid Box

1 What advice would you give about the storage and use of over the counter medicines like Calpol, and prescribed drugs?

....

....

2 Name four items commonly found in a first aid box.

a) .... **b)** ....

c) .... **d)** ....

Accidents and Injuries

3 Fill in the missing words to complete the following sentence.

When there has been an ...., always stay ....

Comfort and .... the child.

4 Which of the following statements about accidents and injuries are correct? Tick the correct options.

A Remove objects from the eye with tweezers ⬭

B Cuts and grazes should be bandaged ⬭

C Lay a choking baby across the forearm with head forward, and pat the back 4/5 times ⬭

D Apply a cold compress to a deep wound ⬭

E A graze may need stitches ⬭

F To stop a nose bleed pinch the tip of the nose firmly ⬭

G Put a plaster on a burn ⬭

H Keep a broken bone immobile and seek medical help ⬭

5 What should you do if a child receives an electric shock?

....

....

Facts About Parasites

1 Explain what is meant by a 'parasite'.

....

....

2 Which of the following parasites cause fever, vomiting, painful muscles and joints, and damage to the eyesight? Tick the correct option.

A Threadworms ◯

B Fleas ◯

C Roundworms ◯

D Scabies ◯

3 Which of the following statements about parasites are correct? Tick the correct options.

A Scabies is spread by direct skin-to-skin contact ◯

B Roundworms are spread by head-to-head contact ◯

C Fleas are spread by jumping long distances onto other people ◯

D Threadworms are spread by head-to-head contact ◯

E Threadworms are spread by swallowing eggs ◯

F Scabies is spread by head-to-head contact ◯

G Headlice are spread by swallowing eggs ◯

H Roundworms are spread by swallowing eggs from animal faeces ◯

4 Which of the following is a way of tackling threadworms? Tick the correct option.

A Regularly worm pets ◯

B Use chemical shampoo ◯

C Medicate the whole family ◯

D Safely dispose of animal faeces ◯

◯

Childhood Illnesses

Signs of Illness

1 Which of the following **is not** a sign of illness? Tick the correct option.

A Raised / lowered temperature ⬭

B Crying ⬭

C Swollen glands ⬭

D Pale / flushed skin or rash ⬭

Illnesses

2 Choose the correct illnesses from the options given to complete the following chart.

Meningitis   **Tuberculosis**   **Chicken pox**   **Measles**

Whooping cough   **Mumps**   **Rubella**

Illness	How to Recognise
	Rash; small red patches develop into blisters, which turn crusty and fall off
	Mild cold; pink rash; pink spots that merge together
	Headache; fever; stiff neck; aching joints; dislike of light; severe sleepiness; fine red / purple rash that doesn't fade under pressure
	Cold / cough that develops into exhausting coughing bouts, making breathing difficult
	Slight fever; earache; swollen gland in front of ear(s)
	Cough; fever (can mimic other diseases)
	Cough / cold; sore watery eyes; red blotchy rash

3 Circle the correct options in the following sentences.

a) Fruit juice should not be given to children with **measles / mumps**.

b) Calamine lotion is a good treatment for **rubella / chicken pox**.

c) **Meningitis / Tuberculosis** can start up to six weeks after inhaling bacteria.

d) **Measles / Meningitis** has a fine red / purple rash, which doesn't fade under pressure.

Caring for a Sick Child

1 Circle the correct option in the following sentences.

a) When children are unwell, **discourage / encourage** visitors.

b) When children are unwell, **comfort them / leave them alone**.

c) When children are unwell, **give / don't give** them your time and attention.

d) When children are unwell, give them **lots of / limited** drinks.

Taking and Reducing Temperature

2 Label the different types of thermometer.

a) .... b) .... c) ....

3 Fill in the missing words to complete the following sentence.

A forehead thermometer has liquid crystals, which change ....

It is .... accurate than a digital thermometer.

When to Seek Help

4 In which of the following circumstances should you seek medical help? Tick the correct options.

A Child has swallowed a dangerous object, e.g. battery, medicine ◯

B Child has a slight cough ◯

C Child has a temperature over 39°C ◯

D Child has red cheeks ◯

E Child is unconscious or abnormally floppy ◯

F Child has a sunken fontanelle ◯

G Child has a runny nose ◯

H Child has breathing difficulties ◯

◯

Staying in Hospital

Staying in Hospital

1 Circle the correct options in the following sentences.

A hospital stay can be difficult, traumatic and upsetting because of…

a) **Strange / Familiar** surroundings.

b) **Pleasant / Unpleasant** treatment.

c) Family members being **present / absent**.

d) A **boring / different** routine.

Making it a Happier Experience

2 Which of the following make hospital stays easier for children? Tick the correct options.

A Being promised a new toy if they're brave ◯

B Parents staying overnight ◯

C Having nice food to eat ◯

D A comfort toy ◯

E Packing their own bag ◯

F Unrestricted visiting ◯

G A pre-admission visit ◯

H Role play about hospitals before admission ◯

3 What is the difference between an emergency admission and a pre-planned admission?

....

....

Regression

4 Which of the following **is not** true? Tick the correct option.

A Regression can affect developmental progress in a negative way ◯

B When they regress, children return to behaviour they showed when they were younger ◯

C Firm discipline will stop regressive behaviour ◯

D Regressive behaviour could be a return to bed wetting ◯

The Importance of Immunisation

1 Circle the correct options in the following sentences.

a) The immunisation programme begins at **2 months / 2 years**.

b) Immunisation protects babies against **simple / serious** diseases.

c) Vaccines **don't / do** make babies' bodies develop their own defence system.

d) Vaccines make babies develop **antibiotics / antibodies**.

Immunisation Programme

2 Which of the following statements are true? Tick the correct options.

A The Men C vaccine is first given at 3 months ○

B Vaccines are given in a child's bottom ○

C Vaccines prevent the common cold ○

D The Hib vaccine protects against haemophilus influenza type BC ○

E A vaccine can be given to prevent pertussis (whooping cough) ○

F The IPV vaccine gives immunity from polio ○

G The Ta vaccine protects from tuberculosis ○

H A vaccine can be given to protect the body against chicken pox ○

3 Choose the correct vaccines from the options given to complete the following chart.

P	MMR	IPV	Hib	MenC	d/D

Vaccine	Protects Against
	Diphtheria
	Pertussis (whooping cough)
	Polio
	Measles, Mumps, Rubella (German Measles)
	Haemophilus influenza type BC
	Meningitis

Sleep and SIDS

Sleep Patterns

1 What is the sleeping and feeding pattern of a newborn baby?

....

....

2 Circle the correct options in the following sentences.

a) By **2 months / 4 months**, 70 per cent of babies sleep through the night.

b) By the age of **2 / 3** years, children don't have a daytime nap.

c) By **5 months / 6 months**, most babies sleep through the night.

d) At 12 months, babies **don't / do** have a long daytime nap.

Importance of Sleep

3 Fill in the missing words to complete the following sentences.

During sleep the body produces a .... hormone, and rests

.... and physically.

4 Which of the following measures can help to reduce SIDS (Sudden Infant Death Syndrome)? Tick the correct options.

A Putting baby in a feet-to-foot position in the cot ⬭

B Not allowing smoking in the baby's home ⬭

C Not covering the baby's head ⬭

D Not using a firm mattress ⬭

E Breastfeeding if possible ⬭

F Putting the baby in bed with you ⬭

G Not letting the baby overheat ⬭

H Not putting the baby's cot near a radiator ⬭

Fresh Air, Exercise and Sunlight

Fresh Air

1 Which of the following **is not** a benefit of being outside in the fresh air? Tick the correct option.

A   Improved appetite ☐

B   Makes children grow bigger ☐

C   Allows children to let off steam ☐

D   Can help children to have a good night's sleep ☐

Exercise

2 Which of the following statements about exercise for children are true? Tick the correct options.

A   Exercise strengthens muscles ☐

B   Exercise improves general health ☐

C   Exercise reduces confidence in children's abilities ☐

D   Exercise sets good patterns for future behaviour ☐

E   Exercise strengthens bones ☐

F   Exercise should be limited ☐

G   Exercise improves self-esteem ☐

H   Exercise reduces the risk of being overweight ☐

Sunlight

3 Circle the correct options in the following sentences.

a)   Ultraviolet rays from the sun on the skin produces **Vitamin A / Vitamin D**.

b)   Use **sunblock / sun tan lotion (SPF 15)** on babies.

c)   Special clothing can be bought to block out **UHT / UV** rays.

d)   Sunblock and high sun protection factor products should be reapplied **regularly / sparingly**.

4 How can a baby in a pram be kept out of the sunlight?

....

Clothing and Footwear

Clothes

1 Which of the following statements apply to clothing for older children? Tick the correct options.

A It should have an elasticated waist ◯

B It should be made from delicate fabrics ◯

C It should fit very snugly when purchased ◯

D It should have large buttons ◯

E It should be expensive ◯

F It should have Velcro fastenings ◯

G It should be fashionable ◯

H It should be easy to wash, dry and iron ◯

Shoes

2 Fill in the missing words to complete the following sentences.

'Padders' protect babies' feet when they are _____. They don't need

_____ until they are _____.

3 Which of the following **is not** a feature of a good children's shoe? Tick the correct option.

A Slip resistant sole ◯

B Adjustable fastening ◯

C Heavy ◯

D Growing room ◯

Nappies

4 Circle the correct option in the following sentences.

a) Disposable nappies are absorbent, **reducing / increasing** the possibility of nappy rash (ammonia dermatitis).

b) Disposable nappies **are / aren't** biodegradable.

c) Disposable nappies are **easy / difficult** to fasten.

d) Reusable nappies **are / aren't** thrown away after use.

Baby Equipment

General Equipment

1 Which of the following statements apply to all baby equipment? Tick the correct options.

   A Baby equipment should be easy to clean ◯

   B Baby equipment should be safe and have a Kitemark ◯

   C Baby equipment should be checked occasionally for damage ◯

   D Baby equipment should be durable and hardwearing ◯

   E Baby equipment should be made from toxic materials ◯

   F Baby equipment should be strong and stable ◯

   G Baby equipment should be liked by the baby ◯

   H Baby equipment should be suitable for size, age, and any special needs ◯

Transport

2 Circle the correct options in the following sentences about buying a pram, buggy or transport system.

   a) It should have **stiff / good** brakes.

   b) It **should / shouldn't** be easy to manoeuvre.

   c) It should be **sturdy / flimsy**.

   d) It **should / shouldn't** adjust or fold easily.

Feeding and Sleeping

3 Which of the following statements about the features of a cot **is not** true? Tick the correct option.

   A A cot should have an adjustable mattress height ◯

   B A cot should have bars 65mm–85mm apart ◯

   C A cot should have a waterproof mattress ◯

   D A cot should have safety catches ◯

4 What can be added to beds to make them safe for young children?

Bathing and Washing

Bathing and Safety

1 Which of the following makes a bathroom safe for babies and children? Tick the correct options.

A   Keeping cosmetics, razors, etc. within easy reach ⬭

B   Always supervising children in the bath ⬭

C   Setting the hot water temperature no higher than 46°C ⬭

D   Having a slip resistant bath / shower ⬭

E   Keeping cleaning materials for the bathroom out of reach ⬭

F   Not covering the hot tap with a special cover or face cloth ⬭

G   Putting hot water in the bath first ⬭

H   Teaching a child to stand in the bath ⬭

Topping and Tailing

2 Circle the correct options in the following sentences about topping and tailing.

a)   Have the equipment ready in a warm room (**21°C–24°C / 18°C–21°C**).

b)   Wipe the baby's face with cotton wool and **hot / warm** water.

c)   **Never / Always** pull back a boy's foreskin to clean.

d)   Clean a girl from **back to front / front to back**, so bacteria do not spread.

Bathing

3 Explain why a baby should be wrapped in a warm towel after a bath.

_____

_____

4 Fill in the missing words to complete the following sentence.

Allow your baby to _____ in the bath for enjoyment and _____ .

Children and Accidents

Accidents in the Home

1 (Circle) the correct options in the following sentences.

a) Poisoning can be caused by **alcohol / sweets**.

b) Choking can be caused by **sweets / medicines**.

c) Suffocation can be caused by **plastic bags / small toys**.

d) Cuts can be caused by **matches / scissors**.

Age-related Accidents

2 Which of the following statements are true? Tick the correct options.

A Four year olds understand danger ◯

B The accident most likely to happen to one year olds is a traffic accident ◯

C Three year olds understand danger, but forget about the danger when they are focused on an activity ◯

D Four year olds have accidents because they want to touch things ◯

E One year olds don't understand danger ◯

F Young babies have bumps and falls because they wriggle, kick and roll over ◯

G Two year olds have accidents because they copy adults and want to be independent ◯

H The accident most likely to happen to six month old babies is poisoning ◯

3 Explain why a six month old baby might choke or suffocate.

_____

_____

Safety Symbols

4 Label these safety symbols.

a) _____ **b)** _____ **c)** _____

Safety

Safety at Home

1 Fill in the missing words to complete the following sentences about safety precaution at home.

_____ sockets. Use _____ guards and radiator guards.

_____ smoke and carbon dioxide alarms. Use door slam _____ .

Safety Outside

2 Which of the following should be done to make sure that children are safe when playing outside? Tick the correct options.

A Keep gates locked ◯

B Lock garden tools and chemicals away ◯

C Check toys / play equipment for wear and tear ◯

D Supervise BBQs and bonfires ◯

E Remove animal faeces ◯

F Put trampolines on a sloping surface ◯

G Have low level climbing equipment ◯

H Don't have plants ◯

3 Circle the correct options in the following sentences.

a) Play areas in parks should have **high / low** level climbing equipment.

b) Garden gates should be kept **shut / locked**.

c) Slides **should / shouldn't** be placed in banks or slopes in play areas and parks.

d) Garden toys should be checked **occasionally / regularly** for wear and tear.

Personal Safety

4 What should children be taught to do if they are lost?

_____

_____

_____

Car and Road Safety

1 Choose the correct words from the options given to complete the following sentences.

EEC	restraints	replaced	immobilised	front

Legally, children travelling by car must use the correct safety ...., which should

conform to .... regulations. After a car accident, the seat should be

.... Airbags should be .... if a child travels in the

.... seat.

2 When travelling by car with children, which of the following **should** you **not** do? Tick the correct option.

A Immobilise child locks

B Leave a child unattended in the car

C Adjust child restraints

D Fit child restraints correctly

3 Which of the following statements are true? Tick the correct options.

A At Stage 3, the child is held in place with the seat belt

B Child restraints should be chosen for the weight and size of the child

C Group 1 child restraints have an integral harness

D There are four stages of child restraints

E Child restraints should be chosen for the age of the child

F Bright reflective clothing ensures road safety

G You shouldn't teach your child the Green Cross Code

H Group 2 child restraints are suggested for ages 4–6

Supermarket Trolleys

4 Fill in the missing words to complete the following sentences about the safe use of supermarket trolleys.

Choose the .... supermarket trolley for your child's weight and

.... Fasten the child into the seat ...., and don't

leave them ....

Early Years Foundation Stage

Early Years Foundation Stage

1 What does the EYFS do?

_____

_____

2 Fill in the missing words to complete the following sentence.

Ofsted do regular _____ and report back to _____ .

EYFS Profile

3 Circle the correct options in the following sentences.

The six areas of learning from the EYFS curriculum 3–5 are...

a) personal, social and **educational / emotional** development.

b) communication, **language / speech** and literacy.

c) problem **setting / solving**, reasoning and numeracy.

d) knowledge and **development / understanding** of the world.

e) **personal / physical** development.

f) **co-operative / creative** development.

Parents in Partnership

4 Which of the following activities, done at home, support the EYFS curriculum by encouraging reading / writing skills? Tick the correct options.

A Pointing out letters and words ⃝

B Singing counting rhymes ⃝

C Finding shapes ⃝

D Making marks on paper ⃝

E Counting items around the home ⃝

F Using a story sack ⃝

G Filling and emptying containers ⃝

H Playing I-Spy games ⃝

Child Care

Child Care Options

1 Why might parents who don't work want their children to be looked after by other people?

....

....

Babysitters

2 Which of the following should a babysitter know? Tick the correct options.

A How to contact the parents ◯

B What the child's favourite food is ◯

C The child's bedtime routine ◯

D How to use the microwave ◯

E How to use the TV remote control ◯

F What food and drink the child is allowed ◯

G Where the first aid box is ◯

H What the child's favourite sweets are ◯

Crèches and Out-of-school Clubs

3 Circle the correct options in the following sentences.

a) Crèches are **often / never** attached to a workplace.

b) You **can / can't** send an ill child to a crèche.

c) A crèche **is / isn't** open all year round.

d) The cost of care in a crèche **will / may** be subsidised.

4 Choose the correct words from the options given to complete the following sentences.

care   **advantages**   **after**

The .... of breakfast clubs / out-of-school clubs are that the child receives

.... before and .... school.

In-home Care

Relatives

1 Which of the following statements is true of home care provided by grandparents or other family members? Tick the correct option.

- **A** They have qualifications ☐
- **B** An ill child can be looked after ☐
- **C** They don't provide one-to-one care ☐
- **D** They can't provide flexible hours ☐

Childminders

2 Which of the following statements are true? Tick the correct options.

- **A** Childminders can come to the child's house ☐
- **B** Childminders aren't Ofsted registered ☐
- **C** Childminders can keep siblings together ☐
- **D** Childminders provide free care ☐
- **E** Childminders can provide a homely environment ☐
- **F** Childminders can pick up / drop off at nursery or school ☐
- **G** Childminders are 100 percent reliable ☐
- **H** Childminders can adapt their routine to suit the child ☐

Nannies and Au Pairs

3 Circle the correct options in the following sentences.

- **a)** Nannies can look after children from **the age of three months / birth** onwards.
- **b)** Nannies **can / can't** work flexible hours.
- **c)** Nannies are **rarely / usually** qualified.
- **d)** Nannies are **expensive / cheap**.

4 What are the advantages of au pairs?

....

....

Nursery Group Care

Day Nurseries

1 Which of the following statements about day nurseries are true? Tick the correct options.

A   They are 85 percent reliable ⬭

B   Children are grouped by age ⬭

C   They provide a very homely environment ⬭

D   They provide a range of toys ⬭

E   Children aren't at greater risk of infection ⬭

F   You can send an ill child to a day nursery ⬭

G   They provide all day care and are open long hours ⬭

H   They have indoor and outdoor play facilities ⬭

Pre-schools / Playgroups

2 Fill in the missing words to complete the following sentence.

Pre-schools and playgroups provide care for children aged .... to

.... years.

3 Which of the following statements is true? Tick the correct option.

A   Playgroups cater for all babies and children ⬭

B   Playgroups are community based ⬭

C   Playgroups are open all year round ⬭

D   Parents aren't involved in playgroups ⬭

Nursery Schools / Nursery Classes

4 Circle the correct options in the following sentences.

a)   Nursery schools and classes provide care from **2–5 / 3–5** years.

b)   Nursery schools and classes **don't have / have** structured learning.

c)   Nursery schools and classes **open / close** only in term time.

d)   Nursery schools and classes offer **expensive / free** sessions.

Children with Special Needs

Children with Special Needs

1 Fill in the missing words to complete the following sentence.

Children with _____ needs have permanently impaired _____

(disability), or _____ difficulties.

2 Circle the correct option in the following sentences.

a) Children with Down's syndrome have a(n) **missing / extra** chromosome.

b) Children with **cerebral palsy / cystic fibrosis** need daily physiotherapy.

c) Muscular dystrophy is caused by **damage at birth / an inherited gene**.

d) Children with **autism / cerebral palsy** have difficulties with fine manipulative and gross motor skills.

3 Which of the following cause damage to a baby in the uterus? Tick the correct options.

A Exercise ☐   B Drugs ☐

C Common cold ☐   D Rubella ☐

E Alcohol ☐   F Smoking ☐

G Tea ☐   H Loud music ☐

Toys

4 Which of the following statements is true? Tick the correct option.

A Toys for children with special needs shouldn't be changed often ☐

B A child with a hearing impairment would benefit from a toy drum ☐

C Children with special needs shouldn't have normal toys ☐

D Toys only help children with special needs to develop physically ☐

Gifted Children

5 Choose the correct words from the options given to complete the following sentences.

academically   development   intellectual   early   same

Gifted children reach their _____ milestones _____ and are

_____ able. Their physical, social and emotional _____ is

usually the _____ as other children. ☐

Children with Special Needs

Effects on the Family

1 Fill in the missing words to complete the following sentences.

Children with special needs have the same _____ needs as all children.

Depending on the _____ of their disability, _____ help may be needed in caring for them.

2 Which of the following are negative effects that children with special needs may have on the family? Tick the correct options.

A Social activities are difficult to organise ◯

B Insensitivity from the wider community ◯

C Bringing the family closer together ◯

D Cost ◯

E Family members may be embarrassed ◯

F Siblings are more tolerant of other people ◯

G Difficulty in finding a babysitter ◯

H Siblings may be jealous ◯

3 What could the positive effects be on a family with a child with special needs?

_____

_____

Voluntary Organisations

4 Which of the following **is not** a voluntary organisation? Tick the correct option.

A National Deaf Children's Society ◯

B Cystic Fibrosis Trust ◯

C The National Autistic Society ◯

D Social services ◯

Helping Families

Helping Families

1 Which of the following are voluntary organisations? Tick the correct options.

A Gingerbread ◯

B Social services ◯

C Home-Start ◯

D Health Authority ◯

E Barnardo's ◯

F Community group ◯

G Church group ◯

H Local Authority ◯

Sure Start

2 Choose the correct words from the options given to complete the following sentences.

community   **professionals**   **needs**   **wide**

integrated   **government**   **parents**

Sure Start is a _____ programme that provides a _____ range

of _____ services in the local _____. A range of

_____ share their expertise to work with _____ and children

to meet their _____.

Financial Benefits

3 What is meant by a 'means-tested' benefit?

_____

_____

4 Which of the following **is not** a benefit? Tick the correct option.

A Statutory Maternity Pay ◯   B Carers' Allowance ◯

C Baby bonds (Child Trust Fund) ◯   D Paternity leave ◯

Helping Families

Health Visitors

1 Circle the correct options in the following sentences.

a) Health visitors monitor **diets / growth**.

b) Health visitors are responsible for mothers in the **ante-natal / post-natal** period.

c) Health visitors run **playgroups / baby clinics**.

d) Health visitors work with every family who has a child under **three / five**.

Social Services

2 Which of the following are done by social services? Tick the correct options.

A They help parents and carers with financial problems ◯

B They help children to read and write ◯

C They register and check EYFS providers ◯

D They help to fill in benefit forms ◯

E They remove children from an environment where they're at risk, if this is necessary ◯

F They run parenting classes ◯

G They work with all families who have a child under five ◯

H They arrange long-term and short-term foster care ◯

3 Explain why some people might not claim benefits to which they're entitled.

_____

_____

4 Which of the following statements is correct? Tick the correct option.

A Social services do developmental assessments ◯

B Social services and health visitors advise on family problems ◯

C Health visitors check nurseries ◯

D Health visitors can take children into care ◯

Exam-style Questions

1 This question is about families.

a) What is a family?

....

.... [2 marks]

b) The number of children being raised by one parent has increased in recent years. Give four possible reasons for a family being a lone parent family.

i) ....

ii) ....

iii) ....

iv) .... [4 marks]

c) Explain the difference between a foster family and an adoptive family.

....

....

....

....

....

.... [6 marks]

2 Below is a diagram of the female reproductive system.

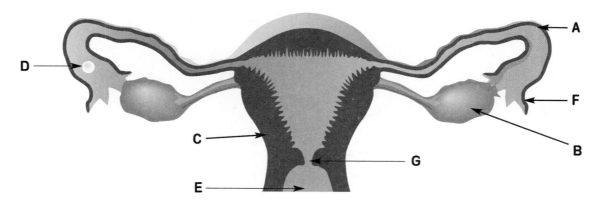

a) Label the different parts of the female reproductive system on the diagram above

A ....   B ....

C ....   D ....

E ....   F ....

G ....   [7 marks]

b) Name the part of the female reproductive system where…

i) eggs are stored ....

ii) fertilisation takes place ....

iii) implantation takes place ....

iv) the baby grows ....   [4 marks]

c) What is the normal length of the menstrual cycle?

.... [1 mark]

d) Which two hormones are responsible for the onset of puberty in girls?

i) ....

ii) .... [2 marks]

Exam-style Questions

3 Below is a diagram of the male reproductive system.

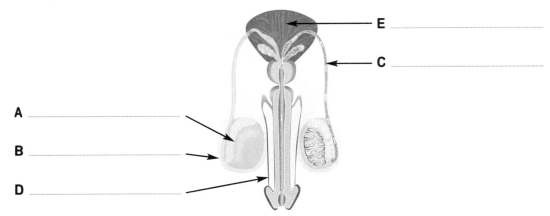

A ....

B ....

D ....

E ....

C ....

a) Choose the correct words from the options below given to label the above diagram of the male reproductive system.

testis　　**penis**　　**bladder**　　**scrotum**　　**sperm tube**　　　　　　[5 marks]

b) Which hormone is produced by the testis?

.... [1 mark]

c) The chart below shows eggs and sperm cells.

Egg + sperm = baby				
X	+	Y	=	XY
X	+	X	=	XX

i) What sex is baby XY? ....

ii) What sex is baby XX? .... [2 marks]

d) What kind of twins are shown in the diagram below?

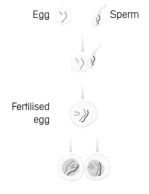

Egg　　　Sperm

Fertilised egg

.... [1 mark]

4 Ultrasound scans are used on pregnant women.

a) Describe how an ultrasound scan is done.

....

.... [3 marks]

b) List three pieces of information that could be obtained from an ultrasound scan.

i) ....

ii) ....

iii) .... [3 marks]

c) The picture shows a baby ready to be born.

Name the position in which the baby is lying.

.... [1 mark]

d) An epidural anaesthetic is used as pain relief by some women in labour.

i) How is an epidural anaesthetic given?

....

.... [3 marks]

ii) How does an epidural anaesthetic work?

.... [2 marks]

iii) List two disadvantages of an epidural anaesthetic.

1. ....

2. .... [2 marks]

Exam-style Questions

5 Many mothers choose to have their babies at home.

a) Explain the advantages of a home birth.

[6 marks]

b) Home births aren't advisable in some circumstances. Explain what these circumstances are.

[6 marks]

c) Explain what is meant by 'bonding'.

[2 marks]

d) Give two reasons why parents of premature babies may find bonding difficult.

i)

ii) [2 marks]

6 Labour can be divided into three stages. Explain what happens in each stage.

i) Stage 1

[6 marks]

ii) Stage 2

[6 marks]

iii) Stage 3

[3 marks]

Exam-style Questions

7 a) When is a baby described as premature?

i) ....

ii) .... [2 marks]

b) Special equipment is available in the neonatal unit to help premature babies. The table below lists some of the equipment and what it does. Complete the table. The first example has been done for you.   [4 marks]

Specialist Equipment	What it Does
i) Ventilator	Provides oxygen in a controlled way
ii)	Keeps baby's body temperature constant
iii)	Checks breathing and heartbeat
iv)	Treats jaundice
v)	Feeds directly into the stomach

c) Newborn babies have reflex actions present at birth. Name four reflex actions.

i) ....

ii) ....

iii) ....

iv) .... [4 marks]

d) A newborn baby is checked using the Apgar score. Explain what this is and why it is used.

....

....

....

....

.... [4 marks]

8 **a)** Explain how parents could prevent obesity in a four year old.

[5 marks]

b) Give three examples of the health risks associated with obesity.

i)

ii)

iii) [3 marks]

c) Describe the possible effects of obesity on the social and emotional development of a four year old.

[3 marks]

d) Explain the difference between a food allergy and a food intolerance.

[3 marks]

Exam-style Questions

9 a) Give three advantages of breastfeeding for mother and baby.

    i) Three advantages for the baby are…

        1. ....

        2. ....

        3. .... [3 marks]

    ii) Three advantages for the mother are…

        1. ....

        2. ....

        3. .... [3 marks]

b) Some mothers have difficulty breastfeeding. Give two sources of help with breastfeeding problems.

    i) ....

    ii) .... [2 marks]

c) Give two examples of mothers who are advised not to breastfeed.

    i) ....

    ii) .... [2 marks]

d) Bottle fed babies must have formula milk that has been prepared safely. List four ways of preparing formula milk safely.

    i) ....

    ii) ....

    iii) ....

    iv) .... [4 marks]

10 There are three stages in weaning.

a) i) Explain what is meant by 'weaning'.

....

.... [1 mark]

ii) At what age does the Department of Health recommend starting to wean your baby?

.... [1 mark]

iii) Explain why weaning is necessary.

....

.... [2 marks]

b) Discuss the advantages and disadvantages of using home made and commercially prepared foods for weaning.

....

....

....

....

....

....

.... [8 marks]

c) Suggest ways in which young children can be encouraged to develop healthy eating habits.

....

....

.... [4 marks]

Exam-style Questions

11 Food poisoning can be prevented if food is prepared, cooked and stored correctly. Explain how food poisoning can be prevented…

a) by good personal hygiene

i) ....

ii) ....

iii) .... [3 marks]

b) in the kitchen when preparing food

i) ....

ii) ....

iii) ....

iv) .... [4 marks]

c) when storing food

i) ....

ii) ....

iii) .... [3 marks]

12 a) How can parents discipline their children effectively?

[10 marks]

b) Explain why it might be difficult for some children to play outside.

[6 marks]

Exam-style Questions

13 a) Complete the table below, which shows stages of speech and language development, by inserting the correct age, or an appropriate example.

Age	Example
	Babbles, says aa, oo, ddd, mmm
12–18 months	
	Telegraphic speech
4–5 years	

[4 marks]

b) Explain how parents can encourage speech development.

[3 marks]

c) Explain the difference between gross motor skills and fine manipulative skills.

[2 marks]

d) Give two examples of fine manipulative skills.

i) [1 mark]

ii) [1 mark]

e) Developmental milestones are checked and assessed. Explain in detail why and how this is done.

[3 marks]

14 a) Babies cry for a variety of reasons.

i) Complete the table below to show four reasons why babies might cry, and four different actions that can be taken to stop the crying.

Reason for Crying	Action Taken to Stop Crying

[4 marks]

b) Young children often have a blanket as a comforter.

i) Two advantages of a blanket as a comforter are…

1. [1 mark]

2. [1 mark]

ii) Two disadvantages of a blanket as a comforter are…

1. [1 mark]

2. [1 mark]

c) Children sometimes have temper tantrums.

i) At what age are these most likely to start?

[1 mark]

ii) What should parents/carers do if a child has a temper tantrum?

[2 marks]

Exam-style Questions

15 Children play instinctively.

a) What is the value of play?

....

....

.... [3 marks]

b) Explain the following stages of play, and give the approximate age at which each might happen.

i) Parallel play: ....

Approximate age: .... [2 marks]

ii) Looking on play: ....

Approximate age: .... [2 marks]

iii) Co-operative play: ....

Approximate age: .... [2 marks]

c) In creative play, children use their imaginations. Give examples of simple everyday objects that could be used to encourage creative play.

i) ....

ii) ....

iii) ....

iv) .... [4 marks]

d) Children who are denied access to a range of stimulating play activities have 'play malnourishment'. Give two possible consequences of play malnourishment.

i) ....

ii) .... [2 marks]

16 Fresh air is beneficial to children and babies.

a) Give two reasons why fresh air is important for children and babies.

i) ....

ii) .... [2 marks]

b) Exposure to sunlight can be dangerous. What three precautions could you take before allowing a four year old to play outside in the sunny weather?

i) ....

ii) ....

iii) .... [3 marks]

c) Explain why exercise is important in childhood.

....

....

....

....

....

....

.... [5 marks]

Exam-style Questions

Section Q

17 a) Suggest three factors to consider when choosing clothes for a newborn baby.

i) ....

ii) ....

iii) .... [3 marks]

b) What features are found in a good children's shoe?

i) ....

ii) ....

iii) ....

iv) .... [4 marks]

c) Most babies wear disposable nappies. Discuss the advantages of disposable nappies.

....

....

....

....

....

.... [4 marks]

d) Topping and tailing may be done if a baby dislikes being bathed, or bathing is not possible. Explain how to top and tail a baby.

....

....

....

....

.... [5 marks]

Section R

18 a) Babies and young children can be accidentally burnt and scalded. Explain how these accidents can be avoided.

[6 marks]

b) Explain the use of the following labels.

i)

[1 mark]

ii)

[1 mark]

Exam-style Questions

Section S

19 a) Families often ask grandparents to help care for children. Give three disadvantages of this childcare option.

   i) ....

   ii) ....

   iii) .... [3 marks]

b) Many working parents choose childminders to care for their children. Explain why this is a good option.

....

....

....

....

....

....

....

.... [6 marks]

c) Explain how the Office for Standards in Education (Ofsted) is involved in the Early Years Foundation Stage (EYFS).

....

....

....

....

....

.... [10 marks]